First published in Great Britain in 2012 by Hodder & Stoughton
An Hachette UK company

1

Copyright © Clerkenwell Films and Channel Four Television Cor[...]
Written by Mike O'Leary

A CIP catalogue record for this title is available from the British Library

ISBN 978 1 4447 6175 7
Trade Paperback ISBN 978 1 4447 6176 4
Ebook ISBN 978 1 4447 6177 1

Printed and bound in Germany by Mohn media

Hodder & Stoughton policy is to use papers that are natural, renewable
and recyclable products and made from wood grown in sustainable forests.
The logging and manufacturing processes are expected to conform to the
environmental regulations of the country of origin.

Illustrations © Graeme Neil Reid
Design by The Book Design Company

Additional illustrations: Graphic novel courtesy of 4 Creative/ illustration James
Wetherell with Jelly London. Worst superhero illustrations © Jake Andrew.
Misfits logo © Momoco.

Photographs courtesy of Clerkenwell Films/ Mark Johnson, Pete Dadds, Hal
Shinnie, Barry Gingell, Debbie Burton, Stella Fox, Giles Keyte, Amy Pickwoad,
Laurie Sparham, Chris Purchase.

Additional photographs: © Alamy:  88, 89, 112, 117, 120. © Todd Antony: 20/
illustration courtesy of Red Giant Projects, 35. © Getty: 30, 69. © Shutterstock

Every reasonable effort has been made to contact the copyright holders, but
if there are any errors or omissions, Hodder & Stoughton will be pleased to
insert the appropriate acknowledgement in any subsequent printing of this
publication.

Hodder & Stoughton Ltd
338 Euston Road
London NW1 3BH

www.hodder.co.uk

# Virtue

## You don't have to be like this.
## You can be so much better.

Stop.

Please.

Think about your immortal soul.

We've just handed you this flyer because we saw a lost sheep. We saw someone in desperate need of Virtue. But most importantly, we saw what book you've just bought.

I know you're thinking it's just a 'soft' book. But there is no such thing as a 'soft' book! This is a gateway book. A filth-filled book version of a cannabis cigarette. It will only lead you on to harder books.

Sure, today you may be sitting wrapped up in the comfort of your own home, laughing at a safe distance at things like narcotics, drinking and genitals. But mark my words, you turn that page and next thing you know... you'll be getting drunk. With strangers. And having sex with them. Several times. In several ways. Possibly with a dog watching. And swimming. Naked. On beaches! Maybe getting high. Getting super-high. Getting permo-high. And listening to 'music'. Yes. Imagine that. Is that you? Do you want that?

You don't have to be like this.

You can be so much better.

# INTRODUCTION

## Is it *always* wrong to kill a cat with a hammer?

Now, I know what you're thinking. 'Rudy, that's an exceptionally odd way to start a book, you handsome rogue.' And to that I would say 'You had a chance to ask me any question and that's what you go for? Honestly? You don't want to ask about the fact that I do community service? (Oh, the stories I could tell!) Or that I got one of those shitty ASBOs? (I mean, that just blows the conversation wide open if you're into politics and broken Britain, all that shit.) Or that in some messed-up fucking heebie-jeebie freak storm I got the power to spew out another (inferior, more moanier)

version of myself? And not only that but by some weird coincidence that comes straight from the nightmare of a *Daily Mail* reading old biddy, all the other lads and ladies I'm doing my probation with got these powers too?' Then I would deal with your compliment in an off-hand and charming way and depending on what way you piddle on a wire we would either be saddling up and heading back to mine to play a bit of Beethoven's Piano Concerto Number Sex or forming a life-long relationship of mutual male respect.

But back to the cat. And the hammer. You see, we had to do that once. The cat had done nothing wrong, apart from ending up a zombie. And even that wasn't his fault. But

was what we did wrong? Was it fuck. In the end you have to weigh up that classic choice: which was the lesser of two evils, a world over-run with zombie cheerleaders or putting a hammer through dear, sweet Mr. Miggles' head?

By the by, I haven't just gone off on some weird, terrible tangent, confessing to brutally killing some old man, just like slipping it in there. Mr. Miggles was the cat.

Anyway, I digest. Why I'm bringing all this up is because it's what this book is kind of all about. Wrongness. I mean, it's not 'about' it. But it's in there. It's definitely in there. When you read it you'll think to yourself 'This is wrong. It's definitely wrong. Buuuuuuut... it doesn't feel not right. Hhhhhmmm. I wonder what Rudy looks like in the nip.'

I guess what I'm getting at is that the goalposts have moved. Some bollocks has definitely come along while we were all having a half-time, chugging back cordial and eating out oranges, and moved the jumpers to somewhere else and never told anyone. What used to be wrong before might be not so wrong now. Because we're living in different times. And we have powers. But mostly because of the different times thing.

So maybe while you're flicking through the book here you should ask yourself 'Is this really wrong? Or is it old wrong? Ancient wrong? Is there a new type of wrong? I wonder how "big" Rudy is?'

And maybe we don't need to find a new wrong. Maybe we need a new right. Maybe those seven sins aren't sins at all. I haven't figured that bit out yet but maybe you just need to see it from a different perspective?

Our perspective.

Love,
Rudy

P.S. Big enough.

# misfits alphabetamine

SCAN IT, PRINT IT OUT, HANG IT IN A NURSERY, DON'T EVER SAY WE NEVER DID NOTHING FOR THE YOUTH OF TOMORROW.

**a** *is for Assman.* Criminals and sphincters tremble at his name.

**c** *is for Cornetto.* The ice cream of choice for burying a corpse. I think it's because it reminds you of childhood and a happy place.

**b** *is for Bruno.* He was too kind for this world. And also a monkey in a human's body. Not natural.

**d** *is for Double-Bagging.* If they're looking a bit rough, double-bag that shit. Belts and braces, people, belts AND braces.

**e** *is for Eating.* As in flesh-EATING super-powered STD that makes your dick fall off.

**f** is for Fight: Bear vs. Shark. Philosophers have wrestled with this thought experiment for generations. Current trends in epistemological reasoning distil it down to whether kicking is allowed.

The bear would rule the ring, but the shark would dominate a UFC cage. Then again, bears are notoriously 'knifey'.

**i** is for Insemination (self). Personally I use separate his and hers toilet rolls for my epic inter-gender wankathons.

**J** is for Junior, Nathan. The ultimate 'Nature vs. Nurture' experiment. I've a 4/1 bet on that his first word will be 'felch'.

**g** is for Gary. Poor Gary.

**k** is for . . . uh . . . stuck on this one . . . um . . . Killing! Is it killing though? It's such a definite word. I'd go with 'creative self-defending'.

**h** is for High Death Rate of Probation Workers. Thankfully, probation workers are harvested from orphanages and raised in vats of amniotic fluid. There's a training college just outside of Wertham and inside it looks like the human fields in *The Matrix*.

**l** is for Lactokinesis. Useful for teatime tricks and murderous rampages and absolutely nothing in between.

**MIS FITS**

**m** *is for Mass Graves.*
As common in Wertham as muck. Which actually is the main component of mass graves. That and bodies. Thinking about it, they're the only two things you need.

**q** *is for Quixotic.*
You could say the central characters' search for happiness in a world where the bitch-goddess Nature has manifested the most obscene aspects of their inner-ego is quite quixotic. You could . . . but you'd be a c*nt.

**n** *is for Nazis, fucking.*
The comma is very important there. Some things are too far, even for Misfits . . . but apparently not for Alisha.

**r** *is for Richard Saunders.*
A soapy-bollocked, tree-shitting legend among men.

**o** *is for Oldgasms.*
Don't you just hate it when you're in your early twenties and then you blow your biscuits and you're suddenly eighty-two?

**s** *is for Shovel.*
See 'M'.

**p** *is for Powers.*
Obvious.

8

**t** is for Tan Lines.
Who says you can't have an ASBO and an all-over tan?

**U** is for Underneath the Fly-By.
Also see 'M'.

**V** is for Virtue.
Could have also gone with 'virgins' or 'vagina-deniers'.

**W** is for Wheelchair.
Good for racing and transporting dead bodies. And also if you're disabled, I guess?

**Y** is for Y2K Bug.
Uh . . . spoiler alert: it's what caused the storm.

**X** is for X-Ray Vision.
Thank fuck for X-ray vision. We would have been bollocksed without it! (In terms of this section . . . I'm really running out of steam).

**Z** is for Zombie Cheerleaders.
I love you, zombie cheerleaders. I could kiss you on the mouth. I thought I was going to have to talk about how many people comment on the fact that Simon looks a bit zebroid (like or resembling a zebra).

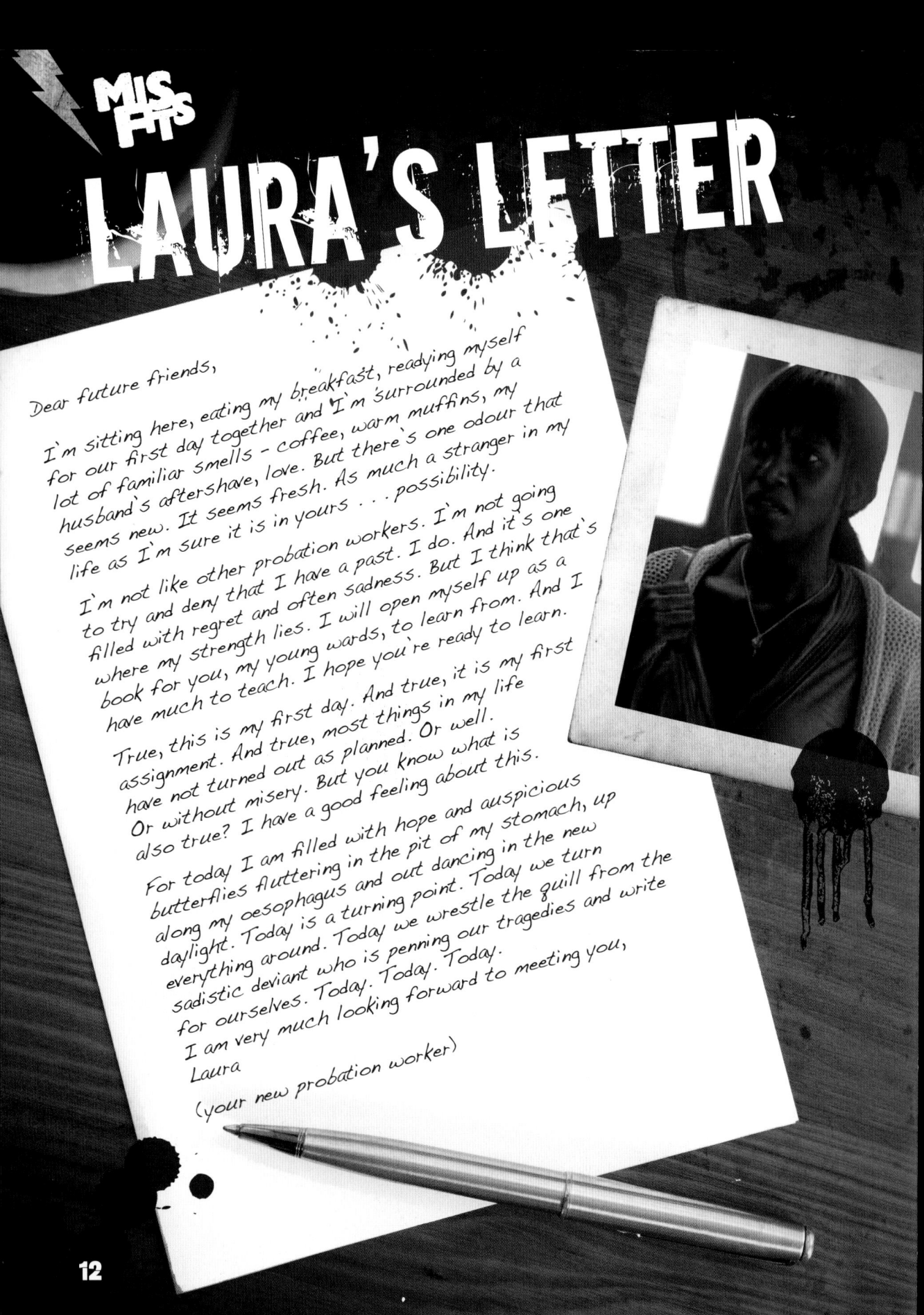

# MISFITS
# LAURA'S LETTER

Dear future friends,

I'm sitting here, eating my breakfast, readying myself for our first day together and I'm surrounded by a lot of familiar smells – coffee, warm muffins, my husband's aftershave, love. But there's one odour that seems new. It seems fresh. As much a stranger in my life as I'm sure it is in yours . . . possibility.

I'm not like other probation workers. I'm not going to try and deny that I have a past. I do. And it's one filled with regret and often sadness. But I think that's where my strength lies. I will open myself up as a book for you, my young wards, to learn from. And I have much to teach. I hope you're ready to learn.

True, this is my first day. And true, it is my first assignment. And true, most things in my life have not turned out as planned. Or well. Or without misery. But you know what is also true? I have a good feeling about this.

For today I am filled with hope and auspicious butterflies fluttering in the pit of my stomach, up along my oesophagus and out dancing in the new daylight. Today is a turning point. Today we turn everything around. Today we wrestle the quill from the sadistic deviant who is penning our tragedies and write for ourselves. Today. Today. Today.

I am very much looking forward to meeting you,

Laura

(your new probation worker)

# ESCAPE FROM IKEA

**107** | **03** | **LEVEL 1**

Help little Nathan find his dad and escape from Ikea. Avoid the paedophiles and use your meatballs to unlock treasure chests and discover hidden birthday presents. Yesssss! I've just won a Himmgrübler utensil divider. Get in!

# DEAR SANTA...

Dear Mr Young,

We are – without a hint of regret – writing to inform you of your termination from our employ with immediate effect. It is customary on these occasions to thank you for your services and wish you well for the future. However, in this instance, I cannot bring myself to do so, both morally and physically, because to do so would perchance involve another child being irrevocably traumatised.

By all accounts you had been drinking. Some say a prodigious amount, especially for a Tuesday morning. And while facts are scant on what exactly you said to the child, sources have provided me with a glimpse into your mania with reports of 'blood everywhere', 'stomping on head', 'placenta' and 'beautiful little funt-nugget'(?) all making an appearance. There have also been references made to wild simulations of copulation to illustrate later points in your diatribe.

But what is beyond question is what happened next. You leaned in – only seconds before the distressed mother could reach her child – and with one hand ruffling the child's hair, you opened that foul mouth of yours and projectile-vomited into the child's face, the veritable fist of spew flooring him instantly. Reports suggest you continued to cascade vomitus down upon the boy. Even into his open, wailing mouth.

My only semblance of regret comes with the news that you are a recent father. These are trying times in which to raise a family and I would never wish destitution on any new infant. But. Since this last week saw the first mention of the child, I have no doubt this 'baby' is the psychotic delusion of a disturbed mind.

Get fucked.
Yours,
Benjamin Lane

# NOTICE OF INTENTION TO APPLY FOR AN ANTI-SOCIAL BEHAVIOUR ORDER IF THE DEFENDANT IS CONVICTED AND PROPOSED APPLICATION
(Criminal Procedure Rules 2005, Rule 50.3)

**1. THIS NOTICE is to tell you (name and address of the defendant against whom the prosecutor intends to apply to the court for an anti-social behaviour order)**
Kelly Bailey, Flat 23a
Wertham Rise. Moorlands Estate.
Wertham.

**2. THE TERMS OF THE ORDER the prosecutor wants the court to make are: The defendant must not: (prosecutor to specify here the prohibitions required)**
The defendant must attend a community payback scheme in Wertham Community Centre. Must report to a court appointed probation officer and undergo a series of counselling sessions with said officer. Said officers will not be challenged verbally or physically.

**3. OFFENCE(S) WITH WHICH THE DEFENDANT IS CHARGED / HAS BEEN CONVICTED:**
The defendant was involved in an altercation with the victim (Jodie Aryeh) which resulted in Ms. Aryeh receiving a 'slap'. It is thought that the incident escalated after the defendant was called 'a slag'. The defendant refused to comment on the issue. (The 'slap' rather than being a 'slag', which allegedly she's not.)

**4. VICTIM'S STATEMENT**
J.A.: I don't know what she's talking about. I think she wants to be with my Darren, is all. There I was minding my own business when out of nowhere that slag, eh, the defendant … your honour … officer … she came up and walloped me. For nothing. She's a fucking – no, don't write fucking down. She's proper mental. And a slag. Tag the bitch.

**5. DEFENDANT'S STATEMENT**
K.B.: Right, I'm just saying cause I know you know what I'm on about but if someone calls you a slag you got to stand up for what's right, yeah? And this time what was right was a slap. Whatever the fuck. This is all that rat dick Darren's fault. You know he's cheating on her? Tried it on with me but told him to fuck right off. Prick.

## METROPOLITAN POLICE

## POLICE INTERVIEW TRANSCRIPT

**DCI C:** Interview starts at 21.42. This is DCI Steve Chalmers with suspect Kelly Bailey at Wertham Central Police station in the presence of...

**DCI B:** Detective Inspector Graham Bacon.

**KB:** What. The. Fuck? Your name is Bacon? Detective Bacon? [suspect laughs] I...I... [Suspect attempts to talk but, unable to, resumes laughing]

**DCI B:** Yes. Okay. We get it. You're not being clever. [Suspect continues to laugh]

**DCI C:** You know Kevin Bacon played a policeman in *Wild Things*...

**DCI B:** Just leave it, Steve. Miss Bailey. I don't know why you're laughing. These are very serious charges.

**KB:** I didn't do fucking nothing.

**DCI C:** Ah ha! Double negative. [Silence]

**KB:** Mate...

**DCI B:** Yeah. Mate...

# How To Be a Hero

**It's not easy being a
real-life hero. Here are seven
simple rules to live by.**

1) Do what's right.

2) Do it all the time.

3) Educate yourself
about what heroes do.

4) Push through fear.

5) Realise your destiny.

6) Persevere.

7) Be prepared to die for
what you believe in.

# How To Be a Legend

It's not easy being a real-life legend. Here are seven simple rules to drink to.

1) Do what's right in front of you: a can, a line, a shot, whatever.

2) Do it all the time.

3) Educate yourself about what legends take.

4) Push through 'til your second wind.

5) Realise Destiny is only one nightclub. If you're barred . . . so what? There are plenty of other nightclubs to go to.

6) Persevere.

7) Be prepared to die for . . . DIE? Like actually die? Nope. No. Fuck that. You're alright.

# STAY TUNED & GET HOONED

## WE KNOW. HOW CAN MISFITS GET ANY BETTER? WELL, LIKE MOST EVERYTHING IN LIFE, WITH THE ADDITION OF COPIOUS AMOUNTS OF ALCOHOL

And not just normal copious amounts of alcohol. Enough to get a baby elephant drunk. A baby elephant who's drinking to drown the guilt. The guilt of knocking that guy down the time he stole a car trying to escape from rehab. **SO DRINK ALONG.**

**A CHARACTER SIPS A PINT**
Drink a full pint

**ALISHA ROLLS HER EYES**
Last player to tut drinks a Snakebite

**ANYTIME NATHAN MENTIONS HIS BALLS/ SCROTUM/BELL-END/ PERINEUM**
Shotgun your can

**SUPERPOWER IS USED**
Last one to mutter 'Fucking Hell!' has to do a super-shot

**SHAUN SIGHS AT THE STATE OF OUR NATION'S YOUTH**
One finger of beer

**KELLY NUTS SOME PRICK**
Shot of Baileys

**SOMEONE EATS A CORNETTO**
Snort a line of rum

**REALISE SHAUN ACTUALLY DOESN'T GIVE A FUCK**
Five fingers of beer

**LOOK OF REGRET ON CURTIS' FACE**
Shake your head, say 'oh Curtis' and neck the rest of your can

**SOME PRICK NUTS KELLY**
Shot of Baileys and lime

**EVERY TIME SIMON TALKS ABOUT 'HIS DESTINY'**
Shoot a capful of vodka into your eyeball

**DRUGS ARE CONSUMED**
Jelly shots!

**SOMEONE IS BURIED IN A MAKESHIFT GRAVE**
Bury your beer

**VILLAIN OF THE WEEK IS FINALLY DISPATCHED**
All place one shot in a pint glass. Most sober has to drink.

# Fakebook

**Nathan Young – Serial Frapist:** 'He was asking for it, with his slutty un-password-protected phone. And it wasn't always me. He was gang-fraped. Gang-fraped, I tell ya!'

Simon Bellamy: I'm wondering carrot or parsnip?
Kelly Bailey: Shepherd's Pie?
Simon Bellamy: Up my arse.
Kelly Bailey: Hi Nathan.

Simon Bellamy changed his relationship status to engaged to melon.

Simon Bellamy: Is my penis definitely going to be as big as my daddy's? Hope so!!!

Simon Bellamy: I am a nerd. I like Superman and talk about kryptonite.
You know what my dog's kryptonite is? Butt sex from me. He hates it. But I love it.

Simon Bellamy: I'm having a terrible day :(
Alisha Bailey: What's wrong, babes?
Simon Bellamy: Prolapsed anus :'(
Alisha Bailey: Give Simon back his phone, Nathan.

Simon Bellamy just 'checked-in' to 'a dirty sex dungeon' with 'Mammy Bellamy'.

Simon Bellamy: Pictures of horse cocks.
Simon Bellamy: OH NO! I thought that was Google! How do I delete????

Simon Bellamy: What does it mean when my farts smell like almonds? Am I dying?

Simon Bellamy: I think my probation worker Shaun is a ride.
Man, if he knew the things I'd do to his balls, he'd call the police.

Simon Bellamy: I am the guy in the mask.
Kelly Bailey: Ran out of ideas, Nathan?
Simon Bellamy: I know. That one was shit.
Simon Bellamy: I got no balls.

comment...

19

# Spot the Difference

Alright sweetcheeks? People are always on at me asking 'How do I tell the difference between you and that depressed dick doppelganger of yours?' Well, there's the glaringly obvious. Beauty. He's the Danny DeVito to my Arnold Schwarzenegger. Actually, he's the Danny DeVito's empty nutsack to my Arnie's throbbing love muscle. Apart from that, here's a couple of tell-tale signs to help you out.

## THOUGHTS

The inescapable inevitably of death, guilt, regret, 'Have I left the oven on?' and Sylvia Plath.

The three Fs. Friends, freedom and fanny. And fornicating. The four Fs. Friends, freedom, fanny and fornicating. And–

What's wrong with you? Just let it go. Fuck.

And the memory of Richard Saunder's balls.

## LYMPH NODES

Suspiciously swollen. Probably infected, maybe cancerous. No. Definitely cancerous. Oh Jesus. I've cancer.

What the fuck is a...

## HEART

Heavy.

Piss right off, you bollocks. What are you on about? Pfff, whatever. Next.

## TOP POCKET

Fags and a box of matches.

'Checking for Cancer – An illustrated guide' and a box of matches.

## BEST FEATURE

Tattoos. Constant reminder of regret.

The one that ends roughly around here. Ladies.

## STOMACH

I'm a filthy optimist so I'm going to say half-full.

Also half-full. Of cancer, no doubt.

## POCKET FULL OF TISSUE

For crying.

For mopping up entire would-be generations off my belly, if you know what I mean? Wink Wink. (Wanking. I'm on about wanking.)

## SOCK FULL OF PILLS

A solitary emergency prozac.

Hammers and Spanners if I can get my hands on them. If not I'd settle for St Petersburg Yip Tits.

# Gush

**Straight from the source to the back of your throat.**

*Serving suggestion only

# Choose Your Own Misadventure

## Misfits – Last Pint at Nabooti's

Indulge in a bit of nineties nostalgia with our very own 'Choose Your Own Misadventure'

You awake in a mysterious warehouse. A dull, pounding bass reverberates through the corrugated tin walls and up into your guts, shaking you awake from the inside. The shrieks and whistles, hoots and hollers of a nearby rave further disorientate and unnerve you. Are they friend . . . or foe?

Then the smell hits you. Fresh ammonia. And old faeces. A stain on your T-shirt delivers the first clue. Kebab juice. The last thing you remember is ordering a chicken shish. Laced with some sort of sedative, no doubt.

You raise your bruised and battered body to its feet. Someone must have done you over while you were out. You check your pockets to find: 1) a silver pen; 2) a box of matches; 3) a novelty whistle in the shape of a penis.

You open the matchbox. In it you find: 1) four matches; 2) a blue-ish pill with an angry unicorn imprint; 3) a folded piece of paper – written on it a name (Alison) and a number (078-'go fuck yourself').

Write these in your adventure book now!

Beware . . . voices approach.

You dart behind a row of industrial barrels. And just in time too, for a man of about forty and a boy of thirteen enter the warehouse and stop just short of your hiding place. The man is dressed in the traditional garb of a Hells Angel.

He is burly, but with kind eyes. The boy is a skater dressed all in red. He has asymmetrical hair. And deceitful ears.

They exchange packages. The boy hands the biker a blue duffel bag. Something inside it is moving. The man hands the skater a brown paper parcel and a skateboard. They part, the man exiting through a side door and the boy skating through the main warehouse entrance. You realise you need to make a choice. But before you can decide who to follow, you hear a screech. You look up and in one of the air vents you see a small rhesus monkey wearing a fez. He is gesturing for you to follow him.

If you want to follow the biker with kind eyes, turn to Page 75.

If you want to follow the skater and the brown paper parcel, turn to Page 113.

If you want to follow the fez-wearing monkey, turn to Page 121.

* Bag of glue and Eiffel 65 minidisk sold separately.

# The Agony
## (and ecstasy if you're looking)
# Uncle (Part 1):
### Nathan does his level best to give a fuck

**Dear Nathan, there's this girl in my college. I really like her. Love her in fact. But she thinks I'm a nobody. What can I do to make her notice me?**

I recommend getting good at something. There is no aphrodisiac greater than talent. Maybe you're not in great shape? Think about starting an exercise regime. Simply jogging once a week can improve circulation, making you appear healthier and more attractive to the opposite sex. Drugs. Have I mentioned drugs? No? OK, disregard the first two suggestions. Think about becoming a drug user. Hardcore narcotics are not just for nights out but can be used during the day as 'personality enhancers'. If that doesn't work, take a shit in her bed.

**Dear Nathan, I think my boyfriend's cheating on me. I've never slept with anyone else in our two-year relationship but last week something funny started happening 'down there'. What do I do?**

I'm going to need a bit more information than that. Funny how? Like you started pulling an endless stream of coloured handkerchiefs from your ladychops? Or did a troupe of clowns start piling out like from a novelty car? I hope it's one of the two because let me tell you this: there is nothing funny about a stiltony snatch. I recommend not confronting your boyfriend but letting downtown go untreated for several months. You'll soon get your vengeance in the form of nightly tears as he cries himself to sleep. If that doesn't work, take a shit in his bed.

**Dear Nathan, my girlfriend thinks I drink too much. Last week I wet our bed after a night out. I just like a couple of scoops with the lads but she thinks I have a problem. Do I?**

No. I once had sex with a trainee doctor so I feel totally qualified in saying, medically, there's no such thing as an alcoholic. Your girlfriend's just a square. And if she can't see the romantic possibilities of waking up in a puddle of your piss, well...
But, maybe, it's the group of lads you're drinking with? If this is the case, you should explain to them that you need to take a bit of time off. Tell them that you have to spend some quality time with your girlfriend teaching her how to drink. If that doesn't work, take a shit in all their beds.

**Dear Nathan, I suffer from gynaecomastia, known commonly as boy boobs. I'm not fat, I'm the captain of the rugby team. I get a lot of stick from my team-mates. It's ruining my life and I don't know what to do!**

Woah! Relax the cax there, Tits McGee. I remember being your age once. And back then all I wanted was a pair of my very own tatty bojangles. Oh, the days I would have spent crashing the yoghurt truck all over my supple front-badonkadonks. You really don't know how lucky you are, fella. But I appreciate that the novelty may have worn off for you, in which case I recommend going to see your local GP. He'll be able to remove a rib and you can try and give yourself a tit-wank. If that doesn't work, take a shit in your bed.

**Dear Nathan, I recently tracked down my birth mother. But what should have been a joyful discovery was tarnished by the fact that she has been living down my road for the past 19 years. To make matters worse, my adoptive parents and her have been having a bitter feud for as long as I can remember. Added to this, she has a son. He's lovely. Nothing's happened between us but he asked me out last week and I obviously turned him down because I don't know how closely we are related. He asked for a reason and I couldn't answer. If I tell him we're probably brother and sister he'll tell his mum (my birth mother) then she'll tell my adoptive parents, they'll get upset and it'll all blow up in my face. I also don't want to break his (my possible brother) heart. What do I do? It's such a mess.**

Beds. Shit in them.

## GOT A PROBLEM?
Life getting you down? In a pickle? Drop me an email at Nathan@seriously-whatthefuckiswrongwith-youthatdrinkwontfix.com

# Old Ruth's Guide
## TO THE YOUTHS

I know I'm looking good for eighty-two. But what good are the unwrinkled face and the perpendicular breasts if you don't have the smarts to back it up? As long as you know these couple of teenage tidbits you should totally be able to pass as one of 'em. That is, if you avoid oldgasms. Oldgasms are always a giveaway.

**DUBSTEP:** The key to passing as a good card-carrying member of the dubstep brigade is in developing a decent 'screwface'. That's the face you make when the music gets to the wompwompwomp bit. I have three to choose from: 1) Cat's Sphincter; 2) Baby Tasting Lemon; and 3) Smelling My Moustache. Feel free to use any of them.

**PLANKING:** This is when you lie face down with your arms by your side in some funny area and a friend takes a picture of you. It's a hoot. Doesn't really go down all that well in retirement homes.

**GIFS:** I still haven't fully figured these out. As far as I can tell they are tiny movies. Tiny, silent, repetitive movies.

**SKUNK:** Didn't have this in my day. We were happy with a zoot cigarette. You had a bit of a puff and everything went soft and a bit funny. Now, for some reason, the kids don't want to laugh. They'd much rather be terrified by the sound of their own breathing.

**SEXTING:** When I first started receiving sexts I thought someone was sending me aerial photographs of the Sudan. This generation is obsessed with sending each other close-up digital photographs of their unmentionables.

**ROFLCOPTER:** I love this word. It's so charming. ROFL stands for 'roll on floor laughing'. So a 'roflcopter' is a figurative term, conjuring up an image of a helicopter made out of laughter. It's beautiful in its fun naivety.

**ROFLCOPTER (DRUG):** THIS IS NOT FUN.

# SETH'S TOP 5 TIPS FOR...
## DEALING WITH AN UNDEAD GIRLFRIEND

FUCKING BREAK-UPS. IT'S HARD TO COME OUT SMELLING LIKE ROSES. IF YOU FOLLOW THESE TIPS, I CAN'T PROMISE THAT YOU'LL BE SHIT-SMELL FREE. BUT YOU WILL COME OUT WITH YOUR JUGULAR INTACT. ALWAYS A BONUS.

**1** *Be gentle*

Break the news lightly. It'll come as a shock. She probably doesn't actually know that she's dead.

**2** *Avoid specifics*

Better to stick to generalities like 'It's the whole dead thing' rather than pick out solitary points like: 'It's the huge gash that you've got across your belly with your guts hanging out.' They're harder to argue against.

**3** *Focus on the future, on moving forward*

Focus on the future, on moving forward. Let them know that – if they want to – you'd still like them to be part of your life. Plan events in the future that you can do together. But be careful not to choose something that a future partner would want to do too. Instead, go for something like: 'When I die, you can totally eat me.'

**4** *Remember the good times*

When you're going through a break-up the tendency is to fixate on how shit it is now, right now, during the break-up. Remind them throughout the conversation of the happier times. 'Hey, do you remember that time when you weren't trying to feed on me? That was nice.'

**5** *Get shovel*

But make sure its a nice shovel. And never call it 'my' shovel. It's 'our' shovel.

# PROBATION PLAYLISTS

PLAYLISTS CAN MAKE OR BREAK THE PARTY. OR PEOPLE. THEY CAN CRUSH PEOPLE. A FRIEND OF MINE FOUND A PLAYLIST ON HER DAD'S IPOD CALLED 'DISCO SENSATIONS'. YOU WOULDN'T MIND THE SEXUAL AMBIGUITY OF THAT. BUT IT ONLY HAD ONE SONG IN IT CALLED 'SMELL YO DICK'.

## RUDY TOO'S (REALISTIC) SOUNDTRACK TO LOVEMAKING

'It Only Takes a Minute' – Take That

'Cuddle Up' – The Beach Boys

'Hallelujah' – Jeff Buckley

## RUDY'S RUTTING PLAYLIST

'Baby Got Back' – Sir Mix-A-Lot

'Get Low' – Lil' Jon

'Where's Your Head At?' – Basement Jaxx

'All Night Long' – Lionel Ritchie

'Sledgehammer' – Peter Gabriel

'Knockin' on Heaven's Door' – Guns N' Roses

'Knockin' on Heaven's Door' – Mungo Jerry

'Hot Pants Explosion' – The B-52's

'Goodbye My Lover' – James Blunt

MIS FITS

**SIMON'S WALK TO WERTHAM CC**

4:20 PM

'Blue Monday' – New Order

'The Killing Moon' –
Echo & the Bunnymen

'Endless Europe' – Kraftwerk

'Atmosphere' – Joy Division

'Stars' – The XX

'Primary Colours' – The Horrors

'Such Great Heights' – Iron and Wine

'Spanish Sahara' – Foals

**KELLY'S GETTING READY PLAYLIST**

4:20 PM

'You Got the Love' –
Florence + the Machine

'Just Dance' – Lady Gaga

'Rolex Sweep' – Skepta

'E Trips' – Benga

'Phantom Pt. II
(Boys Noize Remix)' – Justice

'E Talking' – Soulwax

'Free' – Ultra Naté

'Higher State of Consciousness
(Tweakin' Acid Funk Mix)' –
Josh Wink

**CURTIS' TRAINING TUNES**

H20    3G    4:20 PM

'Witness (1 Hope)' – Roots Manuva

'Jump Around' – House of Pain

'Harder, Better, Faster, Stronger' –
Daft Punk

'Stronger' – Kanye West

'2 Legit 2 Quit' – Hammer

'Over and Over' – Hot Chip

'Running' – Chase and Status

'Do It Again' – Holy Ghost!

# MISFITS

# FIND FINN

Keep the kids entertained for hours or maybe snuggle down in front of a fire with a special someone and get lost together in the hunt for our Lilliputian Liverpudlian. Prepare to peel those peepers peering for the pint-sized probationee.

**So go on. How long did it take you?**

• < 5 minutes: Not possible.

• < 10 minutes: Someone told you, didn't they? Yeah, well done. *slow clap* You've tricked the book.

• < 30 minutes: Okay, I'd believe that. I am officially doffing my hat. Obviously it was around the twenty-eight, twenty-nine minute mark. But still.

• < 1 hour: Totally understandable. He's fucking tiny.

# RUDY'S TOP 5...
## USES FOR YOUR COCK IF IT EVER FALLS OFF

THIS HAPPENS. MORE OFTEN THAN YOU'D THINK, SWEETCHEEKS. NEARLY HAPPENED TO ME. AND IN THAT FLEETING MOMENT OF DOUBT WHERE I THOUGHT I'D BE SAYING SAYONARA TO MY BEAVER-CLEAVER, LITTLE RUDY, I COMPILED THIS MENTAL LIST.

**1** *A novelty turd*
Oh the fun we would have! Leave it in a warm, dark place for a couple of weeks then take it, cover it in a bit of shoe polish and Bob's your severely disturbed uncle. 'Oh my fuck! Is that a turd?! Oh no. Phew. It's just a novelty turd. Oh shitting fuck!! It's a severed penis!!!' Ah ha! Got you, Bob.

**2** *Purse or money clip*
This is an either/or, depending on how, you know, intact you are. I actually got this idea from a buddy of mine, Richard Saunders. That ol' prick used to do a party trick where he'd hide £2.40 in 20ps under the hood. And then he'd walk around!

Now that's fucking entertainment. Not too sure how the money clip would work but I'd imagine it would involve the meatus. Now there's a word we don't use every day. Meatus. Nice word to say. Meatus. She ate us. Around the meatus.

**3** *Hacky Sack*
I remember during those two weeks in 1997 when Hacky Sacks were cool, my parents would just lob me one of the fuckers whenever there was any bad news. Dog ran away? Hacky Sack. Forgot my birthday? Hacky Sack. Nana passed away on the sofa watching *Blind Date*? Hacky-fucking-Sacky. Honestly, I could have survived in an Austrian basement as long as I had one. Even the sound of the little bastards. Kkksh. To me that's the sound of sadness getting rogered in

the arse by distraction. I reckon if my wang had fallen off I would have instinctively reached for it and started booting it about and if I hadn't succumbed to blood loss I would have forgotten all about it in a couple of hours. What cock? This? No, that's my Hacky Sack. IT'S MY FUCKING HACKY SACK, RIGHT!?

**4** *A replacement finger*
No fucking word of a lie this, but there was this lad in Russia (always fucking Russia) who lost his chap in a tractor accident or something and they used one of his fingers as a replacement cock. I know! I reckon they got rid of the nail so it didn't look too fucked up. Anyway, I digress, said the bishop to the altar boy. That got me thinking: if you can do that with your finger, why not the other way around? Yeah, I know, genius. And you'd need a replacement finger too on account of replacing your cock with one of them (blatantly be middle, right?)

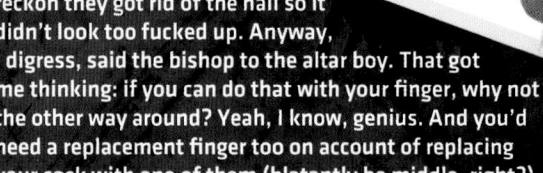

**5** *Draught excluder*
As the cold nights set in you can no longer rely on having someone to cuddle up with on account of having no penis. But you can keep the chills at bay with your severed penis draught excluder. Also good at dinner parties, if you're into that sort of shite. 'Oh that? Nice isn't it? No I didn't get it at Habitat. It's my old penis.' And let's be honest, you're not going to be going to raves or house parties with your Ken-doll mound. Just dinner parties. Just you, some boring dickheads, your penis draught excluder and a risotto made from your lonely tears.

# LADY'S GUIDE TO ... BRUNCH

# Brunch? What the fuck is it, yeah? I'll fucking well tell you.

1. if it's not fucking breakfast.
2. if it's not fucking lunch.
3. if there's fucking bacon.
4. Then it's probably fucking brunch.

# MISFITS

# SHAUN'S SCARED STRAIGHT PROGRAMME

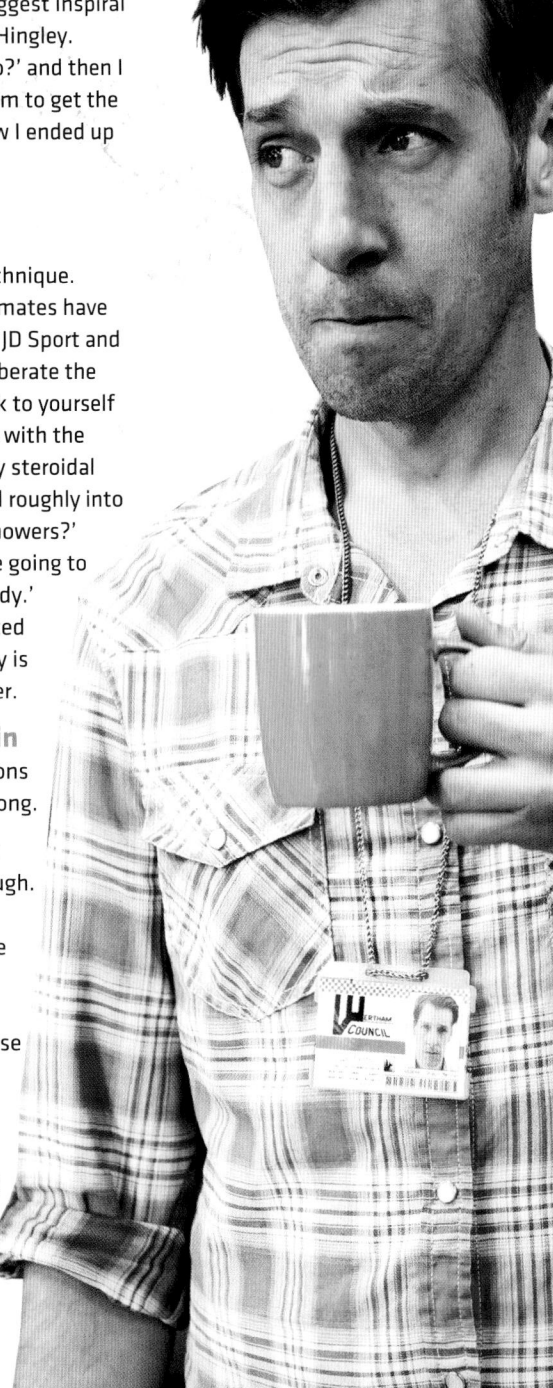

Hello scumbags,
Over the years I've seen many young people wreck their lives with the choices they've made. I see them cleaning shit out of toilets in nightclubs and I think to myself 'What a shame. They could have been serving me burgers. Or holding a sign telling me which way to the golf sale...Hang on! There's no toilet paper!?'

## HERE ARE MY SEVEN GOLDEN RULES FOR STAYING OUT OF TROUBLE.

### 1 Count backwards from 10
We all get angry from time to time. It's natural. Sometimes when I see a teen in my ward on the verge of 'losing their shit' [a professional term] I ask them to count backwards from 10. While attempting this I usually pop out for a fag, rifle through their locker for some weed, check my emails, head to the pub for lunch and come back before the social shit-stain gives themselves an aneurysm.

### 2 Don't get caught
This concept is key to avoiding an Anti-Social Behaviour Order. When you finish this sentence return to the heading and read 10 times aloud looking in a mirror.

### 3 Have proper role models
The human waste I have to deal with on a daily basis usually has one thing in common: ever since they popped out of the womb of the walking can of Tennent's that they call Mommy, they've lacked proper role models. I usually suggest Inspiral Carpets' frontman Tom Hingley. They invariably say 'Who?' and then I smack them and tell them to get the fuck out and wonder how I ended up here in the first place.

### 4 Be mindful of the consequences
This is a really useful technique. Next time you and your mates have smashed the window of JD Sport and are about to step in to liberate the latest pair of Asics, think to yourself 'Would I be comfortable with the penis of Jürgen, a heavily steroidal neo-Nazi, being inserted roughly into my anus in the prison showers?' Now, I know what you're going to say: 'But Shaun, I'm a lady.' Let me tell you this, forced oral sex from Aryan Mary is no walk in the park either.

### 5 Never trust a twin
They are ungodly abortions of nature. Weird and wrong.

### 6 Don't get caught
I cannot stress this enough. Do not. Get caught. You wouldn't believe the number of tracksuited crime statistics that end up in my care because they have never even heard of this cardinal rule of life.

### 7 Don't get caught
Seriously.

# PASSIVE AGGRESSIVE POST-ITS

MIS FITS

Nathan, not to push you, yeah? But you did shit on her bed, mate. I know we all stood by and watched but at the end of the day it is your shit on those sheets. It'd be a nice gesture. She might be around a bit. Thank you.

Nathan, could we maybe talk about Nikki's sheets when you get a chance? I know it was a misunderstanding but it would be a real help if you offered to pay to get them cleaned. I think there might be something between Nikki and I. Thanks, pal.

Seriously, this is not so cool, buddy. I know you are skint and everything but maybe make the offer, yeah? She thinks you're a prick.

You're a prick. She told me you used her pyjamas to wipe. That's fucking rank, man. That's premeditated. Wrong.

Listen up, fuckface. I've paid but I said that you did. You owe me. Big time.

Curtis, you went to the dry cleaners without telling me? I can't believe you did that! I have a tuxedo and a jizz sock that needed cleaning. You are so selfish.

I hate you.

Shut Up
Your Suit

Zip down, enough to just show a peek of cleave. You want a guy to steal glances, not to stare outright. That way it's more effective when you catch him.

This is where your personality shines. My personality loves big hoops.

Just because you've been sentenced to community service doesn't mean you've been sentenced to looking like a gimp. Same goes for a work uniform. What you need to do is work the uniform.

Don't want to sound big-headed but this is how you do it.

Halfway up. You're not a farmer.

Something glittery, urban. Avoid big buckles. You're not a wrestler.

You want to do that whole 'I don't give a shit, I'm on probation' thing. Allow forty minutes in the morning.

# FIELD GUIDE TO THE F-LIST

We can't all be immortal. Decent telepathy is hard to find. And time travel is definitely A-list. Nature isn't known for its fairness – but it's got a cracking sense of humour. Look at flamingos. So let's take a moment to honour those less fortunate in the power department, those whose personality quirks manifested a more unusual gift, those...those...those poor fuckers.

## LACTOKINESIS
The ability to control dairy products such as milk/cheese/yoghurt. Can either be used as cute novelty tricks such as pouring tea with no hands, or to devastating effect such as creating a lethal brain embolism by driving previously consumed cheese into the cerebellum.

## HYPEROVARISM
The capability to shorten the process of insemination, conception, gestation and birth to one earth rotation. From spunk to spawn in under 24 hours.

## COPROKINESIS
Able to manipulate and animate faeces. Often used to create giant Shit-Golems, a large humanoid mound of stools, to do the bidding of their turd-master.

## TACTOPHARMOMIMESIS
When the user of this power touches another person they are able to replicate the effects of any known drug, illicit or not, on that person. Handy for a night out but not really when you have to apprehend a villain and...you know...I've totally forgot what...man, I could murder a bacon sandwich right about now.

## AUTOECTASIS
Thought to have originated from a 'feeder', this power grants the ability to instantly bloat/dilate/distend anyone in close proximity to its user. Can lead from a feeling of trapped wind to chronic morbid obesity and beyond within seconds.

## OCULO-OMINOUS
Creep eye. We've all seen it at around three in the morning in a nightclub or a chipper...the desperate hairy eyeball. But not on this scale. Terrifying.

## AMOROCHANTISM
Once someone hears the singing voice of the empowered chanteuse they look past her hideous outward appearance and fall deeply in love with her. A siren's call...but instead of them being topless Greek beauties, they're total honey-monsters.

## FELICISFELINISM
Uh, the ability to make cats happy.

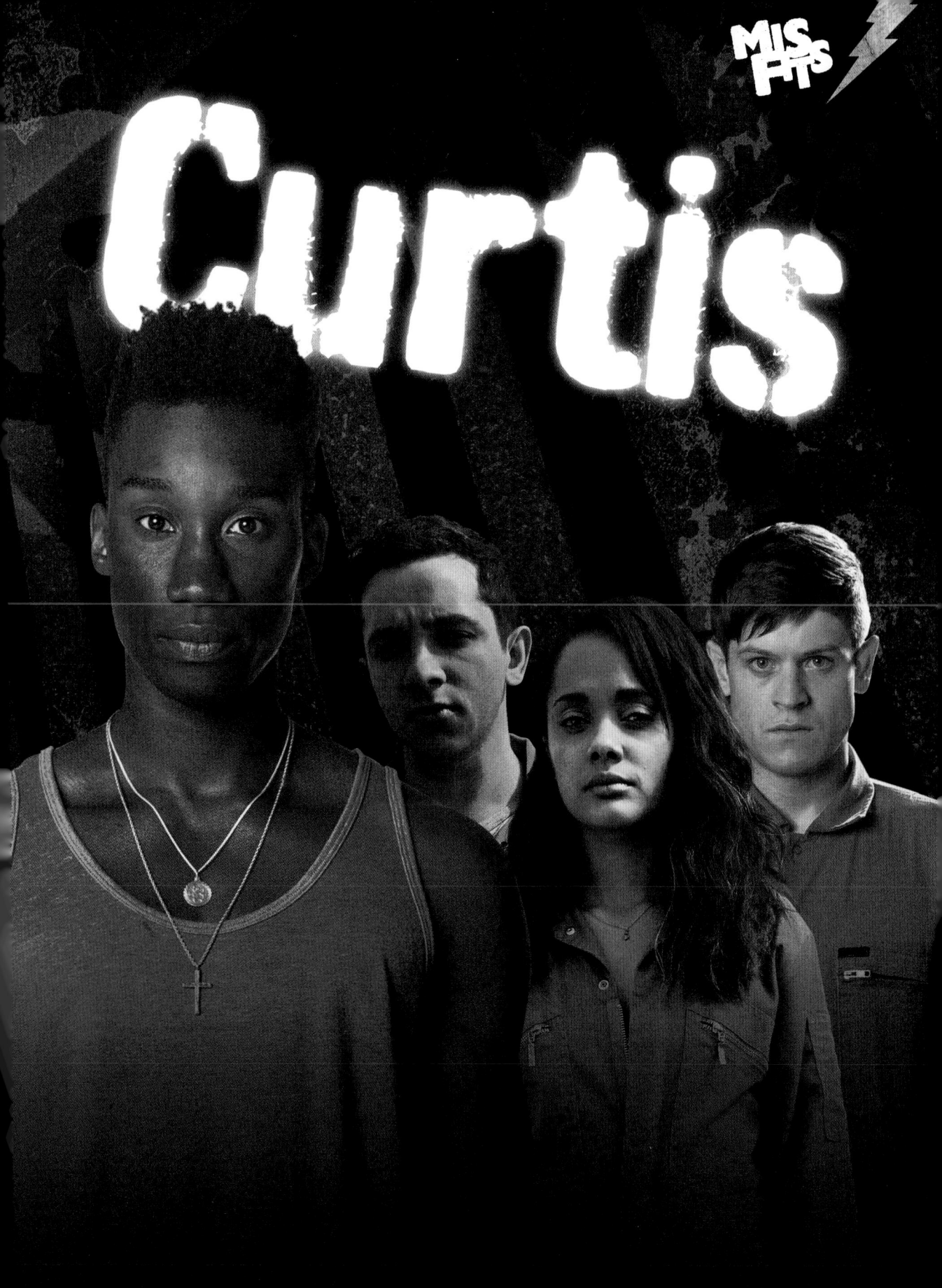

# Nathan's Kama Sutra

## THE WHITE ZOMBIE

You are entertaining a lady friend from behind. About forty-five seconds exactly from the point of eruption you slip out and fake a little death, as the French would say, all over her back (you spit on it). Said lady friend thinks you're done and turns around just at the moment of launch and you blow your beans straight into her eyes. She's rendered momentarily blind and stumbles around the room with her arms out, groaning like a zombie.

## A BANGKOK HOT POCKET

You have a lady caller over for the night and the next morning, while she's in the shower, you surreptitiously jizz in one of her jean pockets. Then when she leaves the house on her way to work, you call her and say 'Hey . . . I think I left my keys in your jean pocket.' She puts her hand in there and when she freaks out you say, 'Sorry, sorry . . . not "keys". I meant to say "seed". I left my "seed" in your pocket.'

## SOPHIE'S CHOICE

Ladies, tell your man you are going to suck his ball. Yes! Ball. Singular. Only one of them. But which one is going to get the love? He has to choose.

## THE E.T.

You insert your longest finger while she phones home. Preferably talking to her dad.

## THE E.T. EXTREME

As above but done on a bike while she sits in the basket.

## THE ANGRY DRAGON

A girl is noshing you off, as the French would say, and just at the point of ejaculafun you tell her your best joke. She laughs, which results, hopefully, in your duck butter coming out of her nose. She looks up angrily with semen swirling around her nose like smoke.

## JAMMING WITH THE JIZZ QUARTET

This one is for 'group play'. You'll need four couples. Obviously. It's a quartet. Come on, keep up... fuck's sake.

One couple are the 'rusty trombone': The lady French kisses the man's bottom as she reaches around and plays with his mickey... like a trombone.

The next couple are the 'cello': the man stands behind the lady, one hand reaching around and caressing her neck while the other hand reaches around and fiddles with her bits downstairs... like a cello.

## THE HOT KARL MARX

What happens if a man cums in your face without warning? Tear out a handful of pubic hair and smush it into your face, working up a nice man-juice / pubic-hair beard. Then insist that 'pubes are the opium of the masses'.

Couple number three are 'the harmonica': The man stands erect while the lady gives a sideways, shafty blow job... like a harmonica.

## LANDING AMELIA EARHART'S PLANE

The female of the couple lies back with her head slightly off the edge of the bed. The male places his scrotum over her head and rests one bollock in either eye socket, giving the experience of old-fashioned aeroplane goggles. The woman then makes flying sounds until she screams, 'Mayday! Mayday!' at which point the man jumps and tries to land his stalk between her mum-mounds.

The final couple are 'the triangle': on the last note of every bar the man taps the lady's fuzzy triangle with his fleshy wand... like a triangle. Ding!

# NOTICE OF INTENTION TO APPLY FOR AN ANTI-SOCIAL BEHAVIOUR ORDER IF THE DEFENDANT IS CONVICTED AND PROPOSED APPLICATION
## (Criminal Procedure Rules 2005, Rule 50.3)

1. THIS NOTICE is to tell you (name and address of the defendant against whom the prosecutor intends to apply to the court for an anti-social behaviour order)

*Alisha Daniels, 7 Upton Drive, Wertham.*

2. THE TERMS OF THE ORDER the prosecutor wants the court to make are: The defendant must not: (prosecutor to specify here the prohibitions required)

*Must wear an ankle tag and attend a community payback scheme.*

3. OFFENCE(S) WITH WHICH THE DEFENDANT IS CHARGED / HAS BEEN CONVICTED:

*Driving while under the influence. Non co-operation with police. Attempting to perform ~~phallashio feelattio~~ oral sex with a breathalyser.*

4. DEFENDANT'S STATEMENT:

*What? I haven't done anything wrong. Don't take it out on me just 'cause you're living in a glass closet. You need to go out, hit the clubs, get yourself double-dicked. No one cares that you're into putting balls in your mouth. You obviously are, otherwise you'd be letting me go.*

5. VICTIM'S STATEMENT:

*N/A – Breathalyser*

## METROPOLITAN POLICE

### POLICE INTERVIEW TRANSCRIPT

**DCI C:** Interrogation starts at 23.20.

**AD:** What are we interrogating?

**DCI C:** You.

**AD:** Are we sure?

**DCI C:** Yes.

**AD:** Are we sure we shouldn't be interrogating your sexuality?

**DCI C:** No.

**AD:** Maybe just a little? 'Where were you on the night of the Eurovision? That sort of thing?

[Silence]

**AD:** Oh my God. I've hit a nerve. You are totally – <tape ends abruptly>

From: Nathan Young < doctorloveandhispenisthermometer@gmail.com
To: Simon Bellamy < iamhere365@yahoo.co.uk

Subject Matter: Dear Barry, melon is not the only fruit . . .

You know what your problem is Barry? You don't diversify. And you're weird. You're weird and there's no diversity in your life. And you know what they say, 'diversity is the anal love beads of life'. You need to branch out. Try new things! We need to get some life behind those cold, dead shark eyes and a bit of lustre to that serial killer haircut. You need to put down the melon and start fucking other fruit.

Pears: Big hips . . . more cushion for pushing.

Kiwis: As furry as a seventies porn stable.

Blackberry: You'll never go back . . . berry.

Pineapple: Picture the top sprouting bit as a ponytail and ride it prison style.

Orange: Split it in half = sisters. Spread out all the segments = orgy!!

Banana: Well, I'm not too sure what you could do with this but I'm sure you'll find something.

Kumquat: I don't want to be uncouth and spell it out for you but with a name like that it's something that rhymes with . . . dukkake? And begins with 'B'. 'B' as in Bukkake.

African Horned Cucumber: Sometimes you just need to ride something to find out what the hell is going on down there. Like albinos.

NO: Passion Fruit: Four words: messy, seeds, Jap's eye, vinesgrowingoutofitamonthlater.

I hope you know I'm only doing this as a friend.
All the best,
Nathan

P.S. Your email address is weird, you fucking oddball. Get a grown-up one.

## RUDY TOO'S POETRY – I

Welcome to my soul.


I stare at my toast, what's the point in buttering?
Hey Mister Butterfly, what's the point in fluttering?
No answer back, he's obviously not a friend.
No ... we all die lonely and alone in the end.


There goes another bus, what's the point in hailing?
Hey Mister Postman, any letters for me that you're mailing?
No answer, just a finger, straight with no bend.
No ... we all die lonely and alone in the end.


A pint before me, what's the point in drinking?
Hey Miss Bacardi Breezer, what're you thinking?
An answer! And with that, my soul begins to mend.
Maybe we don't all die lonely and alone in the end.


Oh. No. Wait. That's vomit.

THAT EVENING, BACK AT THE COMMUNITY CENTRE...
SO WHAT HAPPENS NOW?
MAYBE THERE'S OTHER PEOPLE OUT THERE LIKE US?
WHAT IF WE'RE MEANT TO BE, LIKE SUPERHEROES?
NO, THAT KIND OF THING ONLY HAPPENS IN AMERICA. THIS WILL ALL FADE AWAY
BY THIS TIME NEXT WEEK IT'LL BE BACK TO THE SAME OLD BORING SHIT
OR SO THEY THINK...

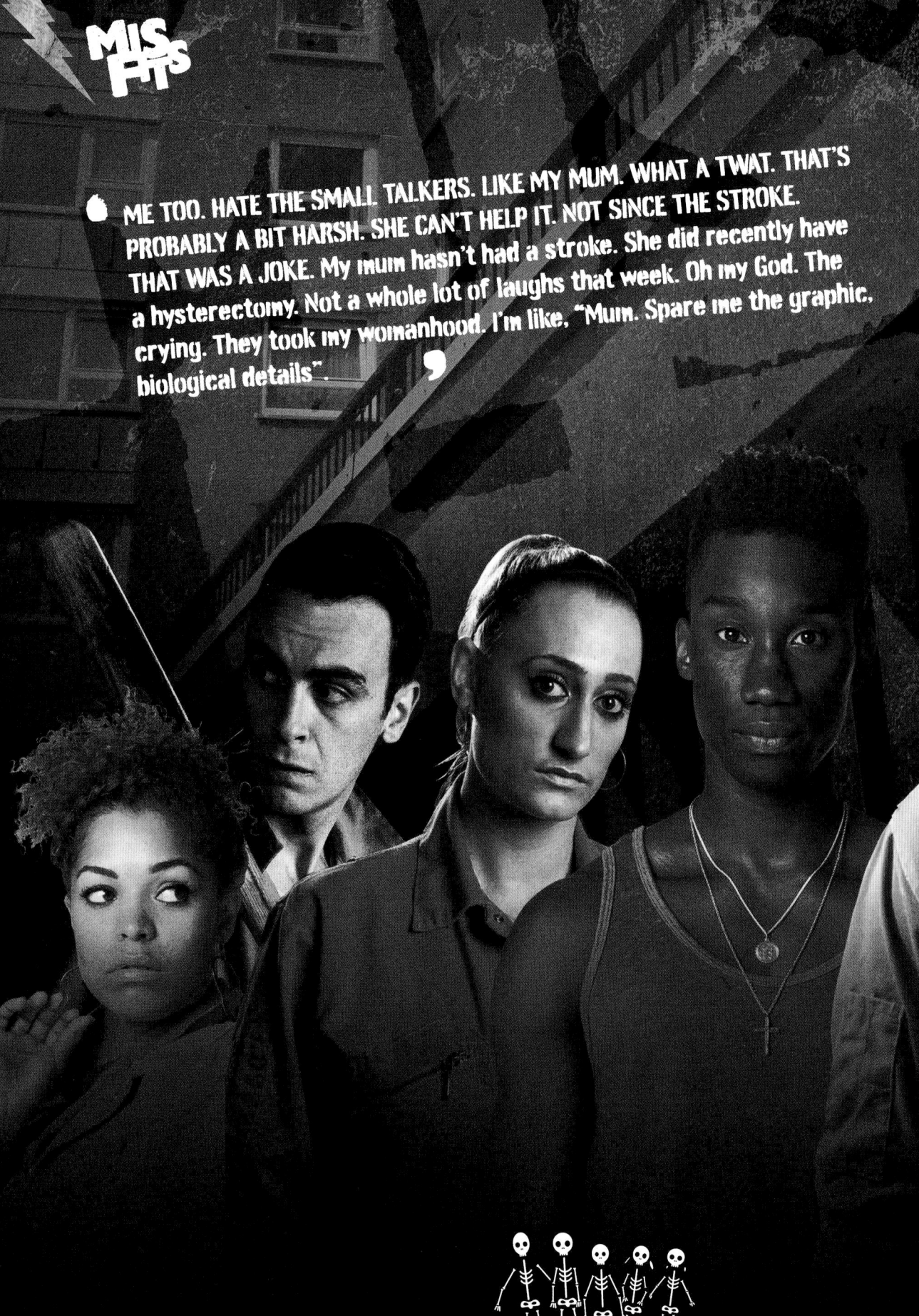

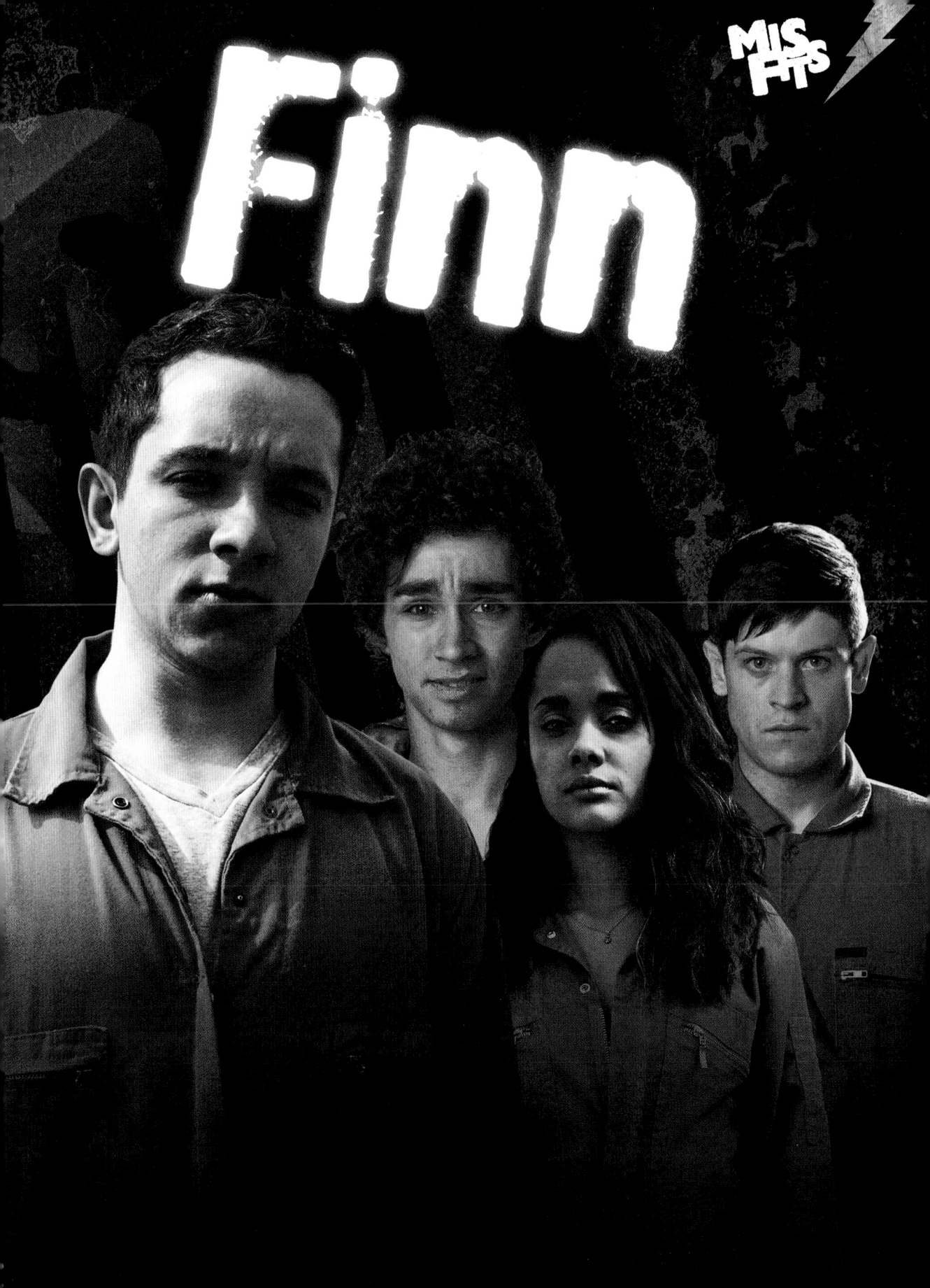

## 1  You need money to be a good dad

Here's something they don't tell you in sex education. Nappies are fucking expensive. I've never liked condoms which is why I carry around the price tag from a pack of pampers in my wallet. If you want a kid you'll need cash. So think of something you can sell. Like immortality. Or your hole. Or you could have another kid and sell that.

## 2  Choose a great name

You hear of these young ones called Apple or Muffy or Peter and you think to yourself those dads have forgotten what it's like on the playground. They're going to get bullied. Fuck it! I'd bully them. You need to carefully come up with a name that doesn't leave room for bullying. Which is why I'm calling our next child Skullfucker. Who's going to mess with that kid?

## 3  Be there

My dad wasn't there for me a lot of the time and he was an awful bollocks. Obviously I turned out fine but imagine if he'd actually been around? Not to exaggerate or anything, but I'd probably be able to cure AIDS with my penis by now.

## 4  Embarrass them

I'm not just talking about forgetting how to dance like someone with full brain function. You need to embarrass the fuck out of your children or else they'll turn out weird. But how? Easy. Return to number 3 and do that . . . all the time. They'll thank you in the end. I mean, I remember when I lost my stabiliser wheels. But it would have been so much more memorable if my dad had been there. Ahhhh, 'stabiliser wheels'. Isn't that how everyone refers to their 'virginity'?

## 5  Pass on something good

My dad was the King Bollock of Langer Land. He was Sheriff Dick of Testicle Town. He was the lone gonad (gunman) on the grassy ball (knoll). I will say this about him though. He gave me one hell of a head of hair, the beautiful fuck.

# NATHAN'S TOP 5 TIPS FOR BEING A DAD

# Cooking with Kelly

**This episode . . . chicken nuggets. Serve together as a main or separately as an amuse-bouche.**

1) Turn on oven, yeah?
2) Turn it up nearly all the way but back a little bit, yeah?
3) Take out chicken nuggets.
4) Bung 'em in the fuckin' oven.
5) Set timer to twenty.
6) Sit down on sofa.
7) Think about texting me mate Stace.
8) Remember that she's a total bitch for what she did to Alan in the pub the other night. Totally fuckin' prickteased him just to get a pint of cider and once she got it she went over and scored the face off Other Alan who's a fat piece of shit. Slag.
9) Remember that bit of blim you have from last weekend.
10) Make a three-skinner.
11) Smoke.
12) Think about the word 'blim'. That's a fuckin' funny word.
13) Blim. Bliiiiiiiiiim. Bli-m.
14) Think about making some chicken nuggets.
15) . . .
16) Result!
17) Turn on TV.
18) Turn it off. Well annoying TV.
19) Realise that beeping wasn't the TV.
20) Listen carefully to the sofa to see if it's beeping.
21) Remember chicken nuggets.
22) Laugh.
23) Check outside the window to make sure no one filmed you to send it in to *You've Been Framed*.
24) Take out chicken nuggets.
25) Turn on TV.
26) Watch *You've Been Framed*.
27) Eat chicken nuggets.
28) Laugh.
29) Double-check no one filmed you.

# RUDY WADES IN

ALRIGHT COCKCHOPS? THE BIG ISSUES AREN'T JUST THINGS YOU USE AS BAIT FOR TRAMP SEX. HERE I TACKLE THEM WITH MY SIGNATURE WIT AND . . . UH . . . AND SHIT.

## God?

God what? Does he exist? Mate, you're missing the point. Here is the point and here are you, way over there, dry-humping a knot in a wooden fence. Look, if he doesn't exist it's safe to say we can bone and smoke and drink and put quarters of pills under our eyelids as much as we fancy. And if he (or she – I'm totally open to the feminist idea that God is a multi-titted lady with a thousand vaginas) does exist we should be doing all that even fuckin' more. 'Cause if you think about it, why would he want us not to do it and then go and invent the bell-end? Or the clitoris? Or the gooch? Basically it all comes down to the gooch, that bit in between your balls (or chuff) and your arse. And it's where both sides get it wrong. Jesus freaks that think there's a God and he wants us to be miserable; they forget about the gooch. And people who say 'no fucking way' that he exists, they forget about the gooch. It's an unanswerable mystery. Like the gooch. That said I have it on very good authority that there is no heaven. Who? Oh, no one mate . . . only a chuffing ghost.

## What is Art?

Short answer: Fanny Bangers 2. Long answer: It is a painting / statue / drawing / photograph that makes you feel something in your soul / brain / womb / balls.

## Do Animals Have Rights?

Yeah, they have rights. To party. My mate, Richard Saunders, the colonel, got his dog stoned before and the little fella loved it. Thought he was a cat. Well, I think that's what he said to me. Can't really remember, I was out of it.

## What is Right and Wrong?

This one's a doozie. Like am I doing the right thing by my friend if I Facebook her sister on the day she turns legal? I mean, if you think about it I'm just making sure that her first time is with someone she knows. A trusted adult. Better me than a team of footballers, right? But here's where it gets all fuzzy as a peach. If that's right . . . when does it become wrong? I can message her at twelve o'clock on the dot but not eleven fifty-nine? Or is that being mental? So let's say eleven fifty-nine is hunky-dory for the sake of argument. Then fifty-eight has to be okay, right? I'm going to play devil's avocado here and say the day before is fine. So the day before legal is fine. It's right. But when does it become wrong? Hours? Days? Weeks? Months? Years? No. Years is wrong. Years is definitely wrong.

## RUDY TOO'S POETRY – II

Welcome to my soul. Again.

Ode to a mole

Staring at me, letting me know,
The fated way I'm going to go,
It's my mole, my worry enhancer.
I have no doubt, it's definitely cancer.

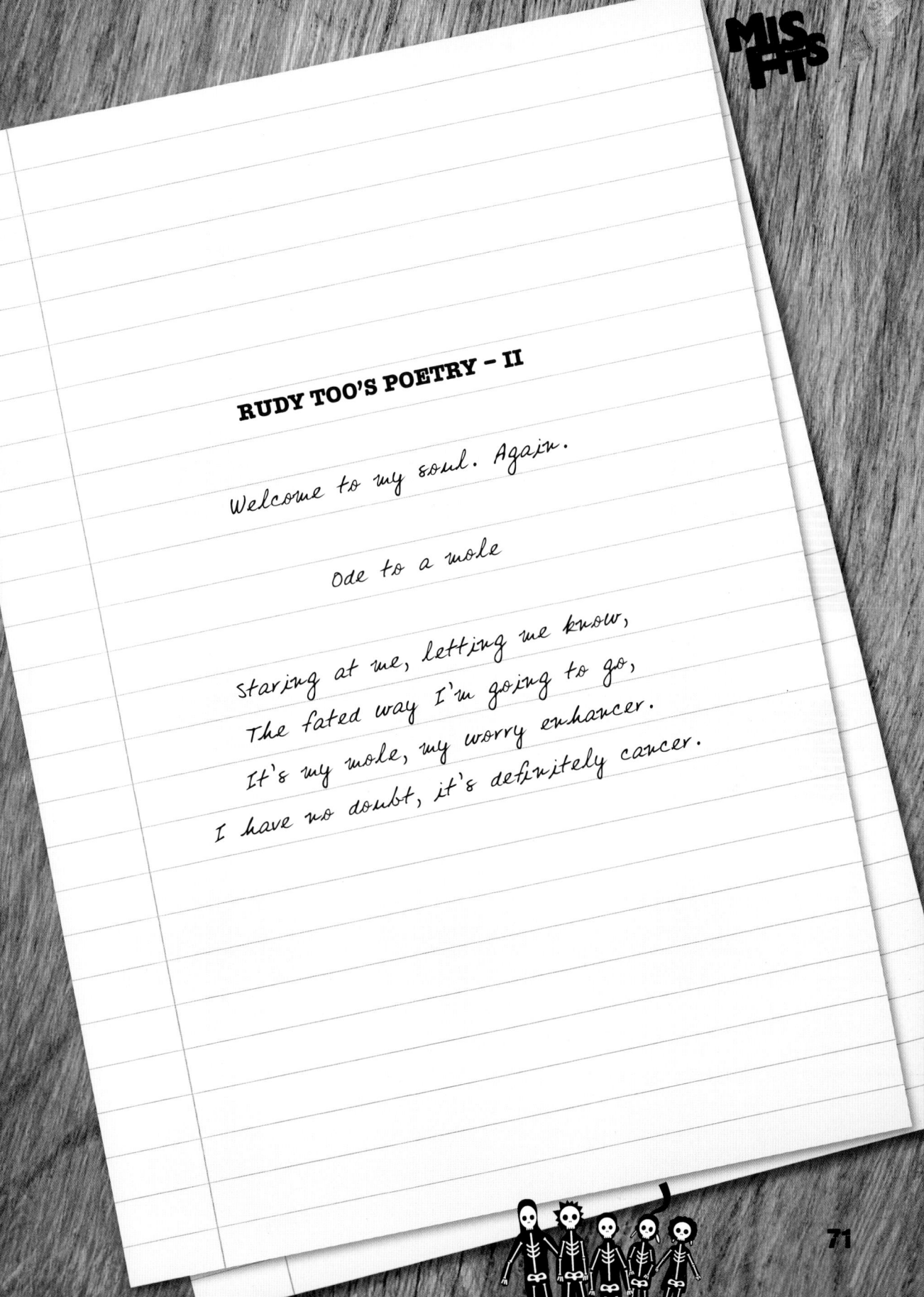

# NATHAN'S COFFIN . . . *CRIBS* STYLE

'ALRIGHT LANGERS AND LADIES, THIS IS WHERE THE MAGIC HAPPENS . . . AND BY MAGIC, I MEAN EXCESSIVE, IMAGINATIVE AND DEGENERATIVE MASTURBATION. AND BY MASTURBATION I MEAN WANKING.'

The entertainment centre. I'm guessing it was Kelly who put this in here with me, bless her sweet little tracksuited heart. Most people would be bitter, angry even, that she buried me with an outdated, shitty model, one with no movies downloaded onto it, and no mobile connection. But not me. I mean, why buy a brand new one to show your dead friend how much you really meant to her? That would be mad.

This is where I go to cry. Well, honestly, it's where I go to think about crying. I try not to as I need to conserve moisture for other purposes.

This is the cushioned mat they provide with the coffin. It is weirdly unshaggable.

**MIS FITS**

The neighbours. I can hear one. I'm guessing he's a worm, trying to get in to feast on my balls. Well, sorry Jeffrey, my balls are still alive. In fact, it is I who will be eating your balls when we finally meet. Obviously, I have never said this out loud . . . because Jeffrey is fucking nuts.

This is an area I like to call 'The War Room'. I can't really see what's down there, but I like to imagine it's Barry's face. My day usually starts with him apologising for twenty minutes for bollocksing up a simple hand grab and letting me get impaled on a spike. Then I explain for another twenty how friends do not let that happen to each other and then smash his face in with Esmeralda. Colonel Hands usually has to talk me down.

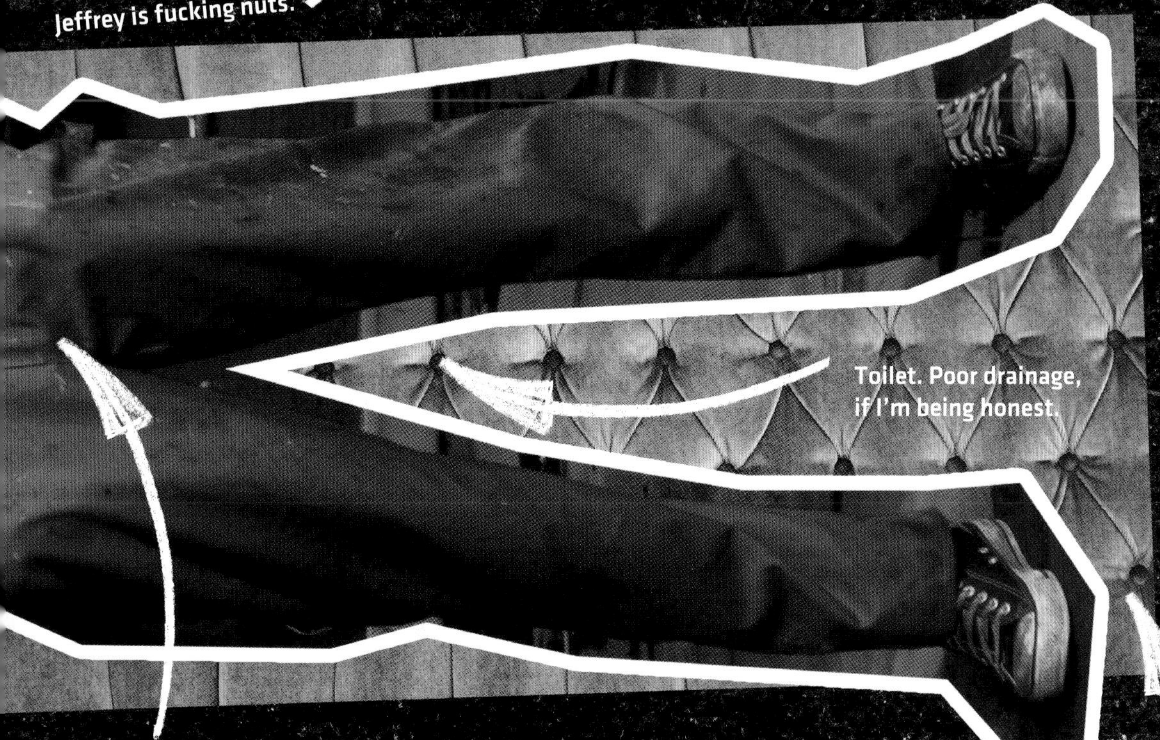

Toilet. Poor drainage, if I'm being honest.

The other entertainment centre.

This is Esmeralda. She's a flamingo dancer. From Spain. With tits that never quit. She helps me out around the place when I've given Colonel Hands the hour off. She's doing a PhD. In being an old shoe full of jin

# Lady's Guide to...
# Head-Butting

NOT A LOT OF PEOPLE KNOW THIS ABOUT ME BUT I'M FUCKING ACES AT HEAD-BUTTING, SO I AM. AND IT'S A SKILL THAT IS RARELY FUCKING LEARNED BUT ALWAYS FUCKING APPRECIATED IN WOMEN, YEAH? HERE'S WHAT YOU DO.

1) If you are the length of a leg away . . . don't fucking head-butt them.
2) If you are the length of an arm away . . . don't fucking head-butt them.
3) If they're behind you . . . don't fucking head-butt them.
4) If they are up in your face . . . fucking head-butt them.

*Right, I'm off for some tea and fucking scones*

**LATERS, LADIES**

# Misfits – Last Pint at Naboo's

... YOU FOLLOW THE OLD BIKER THROUGH THE SMALL DOOR AND OOOF!
HE PUNCHES YOU IN THE STOMACH. WINDED, YOU FALL TO YOUR KNEES.
HE THEN FORCES YOU TO DRINK A PINT OF YOUR OWN SHIT.

# MISFITS
# TWEET TWEET MELONFUCKAAAAAA

## CONVERSATION 1

 **@simonmisfits** Help! Help! I'm being held captive!

 **@nathanmisfits** You shouldn't joke about that.

 **@simonmisfits** This is no joke, he said he's going to cut off my balls and feed them to my mum. He has a power.

 **@nathanmisfits** What power?

 **@simonmisfits** I just saw him turn a cat inside out!

 **@nathanmisfits** Is it still alive?

 **@simonmisfits** Screw the cat, I'm next. I know I'm immortal but inside out isn't a good look for me.

 **@nathanmisfits** What shall I do?

 **@simonmisfits** Kebabs . . . chicken shish kebabs . . . apparently they disarm his power.

 **@simonmisfits** And taco fries! Taco fries fuck him up.

 **@simonmisfits** I need you to bring a chicken shish kebab and some taco fries to the community centre . . . asap.

 **@simonmisfits** Did I mention he has an evil sidekick that can only be destroyed by a can of Fanta?

 **@nathanmisfits** There's no supervillain is there Nathan? I'm not going to be tricked into buying you dinner.

 **@simonmisfits** Aghh, he's got me! It's starts at the anus.

 **@nathanmisfits** Goodbye Nathan.

 **@simonmisfits** Fine, but if my mum has to eat my balls I blame you.

## CONVERSATION 2

 I'm going to a special screening of *Blade Runner*, I've never seen it.

 **@simonmisfits** I've seen it already . . . It's crap; I wouldn't bother.

 **@nathanmisfits** No you haven't.

 **@simonmisfits** Yes I have, turns out he's dead . . . it all happened in his mind. He got killed by the robot at the start.

 **@nathanmisfits** I don't think that's what happens. And I don't want to know.

 **@simonmisfits** Yeah, they're all ghosts. The main man's a ghost, the other fella's a robot ghost, there's even a ghost of a ghost in there.

 **@nathanmisfits** You haven't seen *Blade Runner* have you?

 **@simonmisfits** I have, It's just a load of ghosts playing Frisbee and then Bruce Willis turns up.

 **@simonmisfits** And he's all like, 'Fuck off outta here ghosts!' and the ghosts are all, 'Uh uh, oh no he didn't!' and gang up on Bruce Willis.

 **@simonmisfits** But then Bruce Willis has some like magic Xbox controller and he beats seven shades of shite out of the ghosts.

 **@simonmisfits** And then this sexy lady ghost turns up and Bruce Willis totally does her.

 **@simonmisfits** And she's all like: 'Oooh, oooh, Bruce Willis, yeah, do me harder . . . yippee ki yay motherfucker!'

 **@nathanmisfits** You don't know what you're talking about.

 **@simonmisfits** Yes I do.

 **@simonmisfits** Wait, I got confused. I just looked it up, *Blade Runner* is the one where Harrison Ford is a replicant hunter.

 **@simonmisfits** He uncovers a big conspiracy, falls in love with a lady replicant but it's ok cos he's been a replicant himself all this time.

 **@nathanmisfits** Thank you very much, Nathan.

## CONVERSATION 3

 The unsuspecting prey @simonmisfits sips from his can of coke in the Wertham Serengeti, unaware he's about to be pounced upon.

**@nathanmisfits** What are you talking about Nathan?

 **@simonmisfits** The king of the urban jungle . . . *Tigerus Nathanus Massivedickus* approaches. I can see you.

**@nathanmisfits** Who? Me?

 **@simonmisfits** The prey, with its weirdly symmetrical hair and face like Morrissey licking piss off a nettle, registers the threat.

**@nathanmisfits** What threat?

 **@simonmisfits** This species, *Ferritus Simonus Pantisnifferus*, is famously slow due to its paedophilic scuttle.

**@nathanmisfits** I'm not a pantysniffer.

 **@simonmisfits** Yes, but you are slow. I'm right behind you.

**@nathanmisfits** No you're not.

 **@simonmisfits** The *Tigerus* uses his natural ally, the dustbin, and prepares to strike from behind . . .

**@nathanmisfits** Nathan, don't! It's not me, I'm at home.

In a weird twist of events, *Massivedickus* just got the shite kicked out of him by a mutant *Girlus Furious Myarsebeatus*.

## CONVERSATION 4

It's finally happening. One more day and Alisha and I will be in Vegas. The future is here.

 **@simonmisfits** Vegas Baby! We're gonna take the house. I can feel it in my balls.

 **@simonmisfits** I'll be Tom Cruise, you be 'Qantas never crashed' Dustin Hoffman.

**@nathanmisfits** What are you talking about?

 **@simonmisfits** Me and Marnie and Nathan Jr all booked tickets. First family holiday.

**@nathanmisfits** This is meant to be a romantic holiday. We've been through a lot in the last year.

 **@simonmisfits** We can do the girlfriend shit during the day, then go to the bars where those girls fire things out of their fannies at night.

**@nathanmisfits** I think that's in Thailand.

 **@simonmisfits** What are you talking about? They have everything in Vegas.

 **@simonmisfits** U know what they say, what happens in Vegas stays in Vegas until u go home and 7 years later an Asian kid knocks on ur door.

**@nathanmisfits** I don't think they say that about Vegas.

 **@simonmisfits** Sure they do. And I got this new power from @sethmisfits, they won't know what hit them.

**@nathanmisfits** Alisha's not going to be happy about this.

 **@simonmisfits** What do you mean? Of course she will. She loves me. What's not to love?

 Vegas Baby!

77

5 December 2011

# WERTHAM Weekly

Making Local News Matter More

**Luxury German KITCHEN**

# VIGILANTISM

### WERTHAM ANGELS...
### OR SOCIOPATHIC NUTCASES GONE WRONG IN MIND TANK

Steven Graham (19) had a promising life ahead of him. But last week he bumped into the wrong stranger. Described as beauty-ful by the victim, the young woman instantly turned ag-gressive. What followed was a tirade of abuse. Graham moved to stop the litany of swearing for fear "some kid hearing. It was shocking language." He went to give the lunatic a perfunctory strike. That's when it took a turn for the deranged.

A masked figure in black descended from a rooftop and thrashed Graham

(who volun-teered at a local under-10s football team back in 2006). Once Graham was bloodied and battered the assailant joined the crazed female who had "ran" down flight of stairs. "I definitely heard laughing. And I thi...they shot-up some heroin too" said Graham.

Vigilantism is on the rise in Wertham, with several sight-ings of unhinged individuals fed up with the local police force's impotence. But for every madman with a roman-ticised version of heroism there are several traumatised casualties like Steven Graham. Un-able to leave the house, Graham said his life was made hell by that masked man whose "face I see in night-mares. Did I mention he was massive? I think he was on steroids."

## Illegal Raves
### – A Youth Out of Control

**WERTHAM WEEKLY EXCLUSIVE**

Charlie Billing's busi-ness is under threat. For over 40 years he and his family have run the local dockyard. But now his import-export business faces a greater enemy than the Global Financial Crisis... pill-munch-ing, dubstep-crazed buzzballs. Illegal raves are organized almost weekly in Billing's cargo yards and he is powerless to prevent them. "The police are saying there's noth-ing they can do be-cause there's a public right of way. Bol-locks. They're to-ally yipped out of their minds on meow meow, mud, mit-subishi, whatever you want to call it. Beans, rolls, X, playstations, I don't know. I'm sure there are plenty of other names...Disco biscuits! I al-ways forget that one."

Billings feels like he's been left to sort it out without the assis-tance of the police. "As far as the police are concerned, they're just happy the kids are off the streets. What's it going to take to get them to listen? An OD? Gun-shots? An explosion?"

## BROKEN BRITAIN:
### COUNCIL REFUSES TO PAY UP FOR LOCAL'S CAR CRUSHED BY HAILSTONE

A local man was left reeling as Wertham council refused to pay for damages incurred during last month's freak storm. Jeffrey Godwin's Volkswagen was destroyed when a two-ton hailstone landed on it while on council property. "It's a f***ing disgrace" said Godwin "If someone had been struck by light-ning, we'd know all about it, wouldn't we?"

### PETA ATTEMPT TO LIBERATE DEPRESSED GORILLA

A demonstrator was arrested at Wertham World of Zoology yesterday for trying to free celebrity silverback Bruno. Angel Spitenmeyer claimed he looked "depressed. All he does is look out of his cage all day, staring at free humans. He just wants to live like us." Leave our Bruno alone, crusty.

## A Christmas Message from Father Elliot

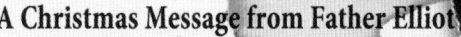

Hello parishioners. I know this is highly unusual using the local (secular) newspa-per instead of our very own Wertham Word to announce a church event but since PromptPrint was passed into the hands of Terry's (atheist) son we no longer get any freebies (typical). But I digress. I'd like to invite you all, both regular and wayward (almost exclusively wayward) to the opening of our nativity scene in our very own community centre.

Now, I know most of you will be busy with Christmas shopping and drinking. Love-making. Gambling. Nothing serious, I suspect, just a family game of poker. Maybe around an open fire. With your children, four of them. And your wife. Your beautiful wife. Probably mince pies. Homemade. None of that Asda bullshit that Mrs O'Brien gets for me. But I digress. Come done. Anytime. I'll be there. Alone. Waiting.

### LATEST CRAZY HITS WERTHAM:
### FLASHMOB SIGHTED

Paris. New York. Wertham? Although details are scant, an eye-witness reports seeing participants practicing in the Community Centre. "All these youngsters, so creative. They ran by dressed like zombie cheerleaders, no doubt on their way to do a synchronized dance to Thriller. Or something." You heard it here first.

# MISFITS PROFANISAURUS

### MONKEY SLUT (NOUN)
A promiscuous member of the Cebidae family, usually not exclusively Saimiri Sciureus. Can often be found in nightclubs drinking gin and throwing patrons the hairy eyeball.

### DOUBLE-BAGGING (VERB)
The act of placing two prophylactics over the male penis, either to delay premature ejaculation or ease sexually-transmitted-disease-related paranoia. See also: skanks.

### BURGER-NIPPLES (NOUN)
Papilla mammaria with large areola resembling a grilled beefsteak patty. Desirable.

### TRIPLING (VERB)
An involuntary eruption of emesis, defecation and urination simultaneously. Considered a sacred myth in some cultures.

### MELONFUCKER (NOUN)
A gentleman who attempts copulation with Cucurbitaceae Lanatus.

MISFITS IS RESPONSIBLE FOR THE INTRODUCTION OF MANY FLORID, EUPHONIC AND PELLUCID TERMS AND NEOLOGISMS INTO THE MODERN LEXICON. HERE WE MEANDER THROUGH A MYRIAD OF GNOMIC AND IDIO-SYNCRATIC LOCUTIONS.... YOU C*NTS

# What I Want To Be When I Grow Up

## Rudy Wade (aged 9 1/2)

When I grow up I'd like to be a fireman. When you are a fireman you live in a big house with all boys. I would like that. I would not like to live with girls. My dad says all girls are like tractors. I don't know what that means. But it makes me scared.

I would like to live in a big house because I would never like to be alone on my own. When I'm on my own I think of sad things. Like dying. And my mummy and daddy dying. And that makes me sad. I don't like that part of me. I wish I could get rid of it.

Also I think a big house with fire engines in it would be cool 'cause it would be really wet a lot of the time so if something else got wet, like a bed, no one would notice and even if they did no one would care so in your stupid face, bed.

I would like to be a fireman because they are big and strong and I want to be big and strong and I never want to smoke or drink and drugs are for losers. Just say no.

Also firemen save people.

Also if you are a fireman you can pretend the hose is your willy and that would be cool.

# VINCE'S TATTOO PARLOUR

## NOT JUST FOR LIFE.
## YOU'LL BE BURIED WITH IT TOO.

IF YOU WOULD LIKE TRIBAL, CARTOON CHARACTERS, RANDOM CHINESE SYMBOLS, A WOLF HOWLING AT THE MOON, A YIN-YANG, CELTIC ARMBAND... FUCK OFF.

## IT HAS TO HAVE MEANING.
## REAL MEANING.

### WE DO MOTHER AND CHILD: HALF PRICE!

ON PRESENTATION OF THIS VOUCHER

## *NO PEANUTS

# WERTHAM Week

Making Local News Matter M...

## DVD REVIEW

**AS PART OF THEIR 'REHABILITATION' INTO 'NORMAL' SOCIETY WE HAVE SOME YOUNG 'JOURNALISTS' REVIEWING THEIR FAVOURITE 'DVDS'.**

### Battlestar Galactica Series 1–4
*By Simon Bellamy*

If you are to get one box set in your life, it should be Battlestar. It has everything. I don't want to go into exactly what it has because I'd have to give away some spoilers. And I hate people who give spoilers. Even the smallest. So I'm going to keep that in mind. Don't worry. There will be no spoilers. NO SPOILERS. Basically, there is an intergalactic battleship called the Galactica. There are also some characters. And things happen. I've said too much already.
10/10

Young Offender Nathan Young, currently serving his community service sentence at the Wertham centre.

### Citizen Kane
*By Nathan Young*

This is supposed to be the greatest film ever made. And it is. I should know. I have totally watched it. Basically, there's this auld fella and he's the richest man in the world or something and he says this thing at the beginning, 'Rosebud' so it was. Then some shit happens. Those of a lesser brain than mine probably won't get past the 'Rosebud' bit because it's a bit f*cking slow so just go with me on this. He's like all 'Rosebud' and you're supposed to think, 'What the fuck is a "Rosebud"?' Well, 'Rosebud' is the codeword that he speaks into

the microphone in his pillow that sets off the nuclear missiles. You see, he thinks everyone's a prick and he's so rich that he has decided when he dies no one else should live. So he says 'Rosebud', the missiles fire out, everyone's like all 'Ooooh, shiiiiiiit', 'Boooooom', 'Aaaaarrgh!' The world's fucked. Then the screen goes black. Up come the words: 'Five years later.'

There's a guy dressed like a priest. But like a cowboy priest. In the future. And oh, what's that? Zombies. With their tits out. Only their tits are still alive. 6/10.

### E.T.
*By Rudy Wade*

Aw, mate. I've just finished it so I might be a little raw writing this. Oh God, his little face. His little face! And the finger! Eeeeeeeeellllliiiiiooooooooooot. Sorry. I need a moment. Fucking hell. Alright. Alright, I'm back. So, yeah. There's this little goofball of an alien. And he is so alien. But, like, if he's alien, what does it say about us? Nah, I'm off again. Oh Jesus. It's just that bit . . . that bit with the . . . the thing . . . you know what I mean. I can't. I can't! I'm thinking about his face again! It's just too much! 9/10

# THE GREAT NATHAN

## ...OH

**Any old fucker can pull a rabbit from a hat. Try pulling one from your arse. Thanks to my new power, pulling a coin from behind a kid's ear is out and pulling a kid's ear from behind a coin is in. Here's my full repertoire ...**

## THUMB FUN

I bend my thumb on my left hand and hold it with the fingers of the same hand. Then I bend the thumb of my right hand and mask it behind my palm, holding the top of my hand out towards the **'muuuuuh'** (what magicians call the person you're performing to). Then I place the left thumb on top of the right thumb's knuckle and move it up and down. It gives the illusion that the thumb is all fucked up. For the finale I throw my left thumb into the air and it disappears. Imagine the muuuuuh's surprise when they can feel a wriggling in their arse. That's right folks ... I've magicked my severed thumb up their arse. Thank you!

## THE QUEEN OF FARTS

I take a regular deck of cards. I shuffle, cut the deck, spread it out like a fan. I ask the muuuuuh to pick one but before they get a chance I say, **'Before you pick one of my cards, maybe you should pick the card from between your butt cheeks?'** and pazaaaah! Fucking card in their colon. I'm here all week!

## THE WANDERING WAND

I build up the suspense by warning the muuuuuh what they are about to see shouldn't be witnessed by people with heart conditions or the pregnant. It's a nice little touch of showmanship. I spin them a yarn about how the last man that attempted this died or some guff. Then I start to look around and say, **'Hang on, I can't do it without my wand.'** They start to look but they obviously haven't seen it. I say, **'Are you sure ...'** – hold it for dramatic effect – **'... you are not sitting on it?'** Boom. Wand up their hole. Tip your waitress, cocknose.

## BIRD

I ask them the time. Then I put a live bird inside them . . . with magic. Oh no, I didn't! Yeah. Yeah, I did!

## THE VENTRILOQUIST'S BUMMY

I have this ventriloquist dummy. Freaky looking langer. Actually kind of reminds me of someone I know. Same symmetrical hair and cold, dead, shark eyes. Anyway. I get this dummy and I do the whole 'rottle of reer' routine. It's the old bait and switch. This goes on for a bit. Then, for 'the prestige' I drink a glass of water while singing 'The Irish Rover'. Once I've finished the water, I get the dummy to say **'Can you call an ambulance?'** They ask why and I finish with: **'Where did my glass go?'** . . .

## AND HERE'S SOMETHING FOR YOURSELF TO PRACTISE AT HOME . . .

Alright, grand, not technically magic but it's some proper Derren Brown mind-warp shit. It's to do with your taste buds and memory. Basically, if you close your eyes and pretend to shake a salt-shaker into your mouth, it fools your own brain and you can actually taste the salt. Go on . . .

NO ONE'S LOOKING.

TRY IT.

TRY IT NOW.

NOW, TRY IT ON YOUR GRAN.

**MIS FITS**

WE'RE YOUNG. WE'RE SUPPOSED TO DRINK TOO MUCH. WE'RE SUPPOSED TO HAVE BAD ATTITUDES AND SHAG EACH OTHER'S BRAINS OUT. We were designed to party. We owe it to ourselves to party hard. We owe it to each other. This is it. This is our time. So a few of us will overdose, or go mental. Charles Darwin said you can't make an omelette without breaking a few eggs. That's what it's about — breaking eggs — by eggs, I mean, getting twatted. **"**

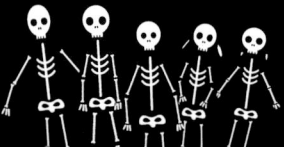

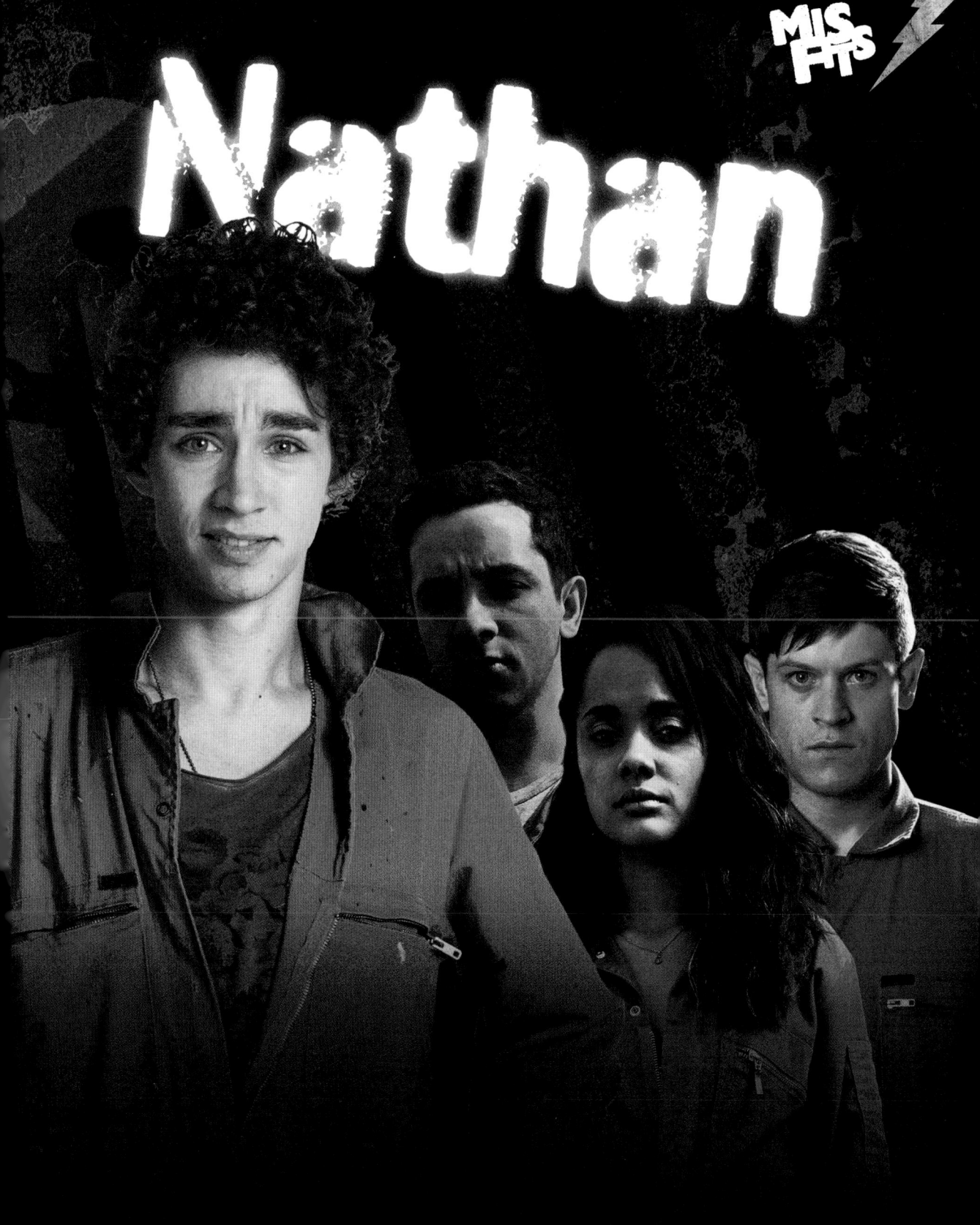

Nathan

MIS FITS

# MISFITS

# POWERS THROUGH TIME WITH NATHAN

You think this is the first time that one of those fucked-up storms happened? Poppy-cock. That's right, cockchops, poppycock. Luckily for you there's a scholar of history here to take you on a journey through time. And by 'scholar' I mean 'someone who copied and pasted a weird email Barry sent'.

Look at this. It goes without saying that whoever drew this is a fucking lad. He's got the power of flight and probably some sort of laser-eyes shit going on and what does he do? Fly around drawing massive boners. Fucking lad. If he was around today he'd totes be playing rugby. Lad.

This is clearly evidence of some form of time travel. Undeniably. How do I know? Well, ecstasy wasn't invented until the 1970s. And look at them here. Off . . . their . . . tits. They are loving it.

If I could be sent back to any time with a power it would probably be the Victorian era. Ah Jesus. The laugh you'd have. They were a very gullible people, very skittish. Sure, look at this fella. He's only having a laugh. Jumping around, giving the occasional 'Here! You!' or a 'Waaaahooo!' They didn't appreciate it. Very serious. Although, I'm not too sure what's going on down there . . . is he flashing a dead body? Pointless at best.

You have to remember at the time this painting was done, there was no real massage and holistic treatment industry. When this lady here got given the power to make a little massage gimp-monkey appear whenever she wanted, people were shocked to say the least. They thought the little fella was attacking her. But look at her. She's grand. She's not dead or unconscious . . . she's just super relaxed.

I only know what's going on in this picture because having been raised a Catholic we were force-fed all the saints' life stories, vital stats and Desert Island Discs. This chief here is St Bartholomew. Legend has it he never went thirsty a day in his life. He'd be praying away and he'd need to rehydrate so he'd look around for a statue with teats and wham! Instant electrolytes. For centuries they thought it was some form of divine milk but a few years later they found a vial of the stuff buried with him and brought it to a lab. Irn-Bru, apparently.

# RUDY TOO'S POETRY – III

Welcome (back) to my soul.

## I can hear you ...

I can hear you, you know; I'm not asleep,
So stop what you're doing underneath your sheet.
Just because we look the same doesn't make it okay.
It still makes me sad, hearing you cough and then spray.

I can hear you, you know, and it's getting me down.
It's dark, true, but that doesn't mean I won't frown.
And I know you'll say, 'Relax! It's just a Tom Hanks,'
But that doesn't mean it doesn't give me existential angst.

I can hear you, you know; this has got to stop,
I'm tired of waiting to sleep 'til after you pop.
It's unhealthy and wrong and there's no point lying,
I think it's weird that you do it while I'm sitting up crying.

# SIMON'S
# X OR Y

## Simon's Choice

Simon puts to bed some age-old rivalries. Think Celtic and Rangers with way more bloody noses and, oddly, much less physical violence.

### Stars Wars or Star Trek?

Trek. Wars was like getting to know someone and becoming friends and going over to their house for sleepovers and then one day you saw a home video and you found out about this whole past you never knew existed. And in this past they were Nazi sympathisers. And had sex with their sister. You wish you could forget about the past and only remember why you became friends . . . but it's always going to be there. It's always going to be there.

### Kirk or Picard?

Picard. Kirk cheated in the Kobayashi Maru.

### Data or C-3PO?

Data. C-3PO would stress me out. Also if I came into probation with him I can imagine the type of thing Nathan would say. Lots of jokes about loving disco music and, um, lube.

### Ryu or Ken?

Ryu. Ken always freaked me out a bit. I think he wanted to be Ryu a little bit too much if you know what I mean? I think Ken would try on Ryu's gi and not tell him if he could. Like if they were sharing a hotel room, for example.

### Jean Grey or Emma Frost?

Emma Frost. See the Gwen Stacey answer. I'm not that good with loss. And Jean Grey is multiple loss.

### BSG or SG-1?

By the Gods of Kobol, a thousand times BSG.

### Marvel or DC?

Marvel... they're my kind of heroes.

### Gwen Stacey or Mary Jane Watson?

Gwen Stacey was his first love. Although I don't know what I'd do if someone killed my girlfriend.

### Buffy or Faith?

Trick question. The real rivalry is between Willow Rosenberg and Cordelia Chase. I'm a WR man. Minus the going evil and flailing people thing.

### Starbuck or Seven of Nine?

I think I'd have more in common with Seven of Nine. She seems more like a girl who would be happy to sit in and watch an episode of Battlestar.

### One bullet... Wesley Crusher or Jar Jar?

I would never condone killing people. But I would line them both up and use the same bullet to end them both. They are not people.

### Warhammer or 40k?

Too far.

**91**

# MISFITS! ACTION FORCE!

Interchangeable heads – two toys for the price of one!

Eagle-eye-rolling action.

Moveable finger – for 'feeding the pony' action.

Pull string and hear her tut!

Now with added sarcasm.

Detachable cocks – normal AND rotting!

Warning: choking hazard (detachable cocks).

The only doll on the market this Christmas with major trust issues.

93

Here's a list of those telltale signs that your boyfriend is a secret superhero.

ARE YOU DATING A PART-TIME NIGHT-TIME SUPERHERO

1. When you ask him where he's been he makes slits of his eyes and singsongs: 'No . . . where.'

2. Uses the word destiny a lot. Even at breakfast.

3. Has a fondness for standing on rooftops.

4. Just after sex he'll suddenly look afraid and say, 'You know I'll never hurt you . . .' Yeah, cheers. Wasn't thinking of it until you said it.

5. Hums: 'Duh duh duuuuuuuuh . . .' when receiving news.

6. Has unexplained bloody knuckles.

7. Has unexplained black eyes.

8. Has unexplained gunshot wounds.

9. Complains that something is 'too quiet . . .'

10. Gets a birthday card from someone you've never met called 'Your Nemesis'.

11. You occasionally wake up next to an arranged pile of pillows and a tape recorder playing snoring sounds.

12. Sometimes when you're sitting in Burger King he'll say, 'Do you trust me?! We have to leave. Now!' and then never mention it again.

13. He shakes his fist at nothing in particular. Just thin air.

14. Sometimes you'll come back to the flat and he'll be in the bedroom and the door will be locked and he'll tell you to 'go away! I'm wanking' but it doesn't sound like he's wanking, it sounds like he's making playfight sounds and then undressing and putting something down the back of your wardrobe.

15. You find a vigilante costume down the back of your wardrobe.

## RUDY TOO'S POETRY – IV

So yeah. My soul.

## Haiku

Autumn evening.
The crisp crunch of scarlet leaves.
Soft squelch of dog poo.

# NATHAN'S PRISON LETTERS

Dear Doreen,

I'll be honest, I always thought people who wrote to prisoners were nutbars. Or at least morbidly obese. I can tell you are neither. You sound pretty together. And you wrote your letter using a pen. So unless it was one of those fat pens, I think we're going to get along grand.

Settling in to prison is going fine. The trick is first impressions. Take, for example, the first time you go for a group shower. If you walk in all timid and nervous, the next few years will be hell. You need to sashay in there like getting into those showers is the reason you committed the crime. And then crap yourself. If there's one thing I've learned about prison it's that no one wants to mess with a hungry power-bottom covered in shit. And you don't learn that watching *The Shawshank Redemption*.

The only 'drama' I've had to put up with is from my cellmate, Aryan Joe. He keeps telling me that his best friend Mister Stabby (the fork he keeps under his pillow) is getting very jealous of the way Aryan Joe is looking at my lips. I haven't figured out if that's supposed to be a threat or a compliment. Will keep you posted.

Yours, in prison,
Nathan Young Esquire

Doreeeeeeeeeeeen,

Okay, that was only the second letter from you, so I still haven't figured out your sense of humour. But I think that could have been one of the funniest things anyone has ever written. Very nuanced. Very dark. Very ironic. Very dry.

Obviously I'm not going to go through all your questions because 1) you were joking; and 2) I have limited access to the library so I can't go and look up who these two fellas Balberith and Malaphar are and why exactly they would be talking to my testes as I sleep. I'll bet you are a right laugh to get stoned with.

Speaking of laughs, finally met Mister Stabby. He's a fucking hoot. We got that whole 'lip' thing sorted. Don't tell Aryan Joe this, but I actually kind of sort of prefer The Stabster.

I'll see you at the jaws of the beast (Get it? Because of that thing you said? I used to hate really 'ironic' twats but it is actually good fun).

Nathan

Listen Crazytits,

If you come anywhere near us, Mister Stabby is going to show you how he got his name. His first name. Which is 'Iwillcallthepolice'.

You can't go around saying shit like that to poor prisoners like us. Aryan Joe had a read of your letter and he hasn't left his bed in days. This is the worst he's ever felt. And he got the most aggressive form of food poisoning the prison doctors had ever seen after he ate Mexico Dave's ear. You need to sort yourself out.

So until then I'm terminating our letter friendship.

Nathan
P.S. I'm beginning to doubt you're the svelte beauty I have in my mind.

# COMMUNITY SERVICE SCHEDULE

| Time/Day | Monday | Tuesday | Wednesday | Thursday | Friday |
|---|---|---|---|---|---|
| 9.00 | Shit: picking it up. | Shit: Unblocking it. | Shit: Sorting through it. | Shit: Fixing it. | Shit*: Pac it. |
| 10.00 | Anger Management: i.e. if you manage to stay out of my sight, I won't get angry. | | | | |
| 11.00 | Graffiti: All tags. | Graffiti: All stencils. | Graffiti: All slogans. | Graffiti: All bell-ends. | Graffiti: Mor bell-ends. |
| 12.00 | Putting out the chairs for WeightWatchers. | Putting out the chairs for Alcoholics Anonymous. | Putting out the chairs for Gamblers Anonymous. | Putting out the chairs for a clairvoyant. | Putting out the chairs for my own personal enjoyment and making them fight. |
| | I have set this time apart for you to reflect in silence on the sacred privacy of Shaun's office. You may also eat your lunch. | | | | |

\* I use the term 'shit' loosely. Most 'shit' is TBC on the day.

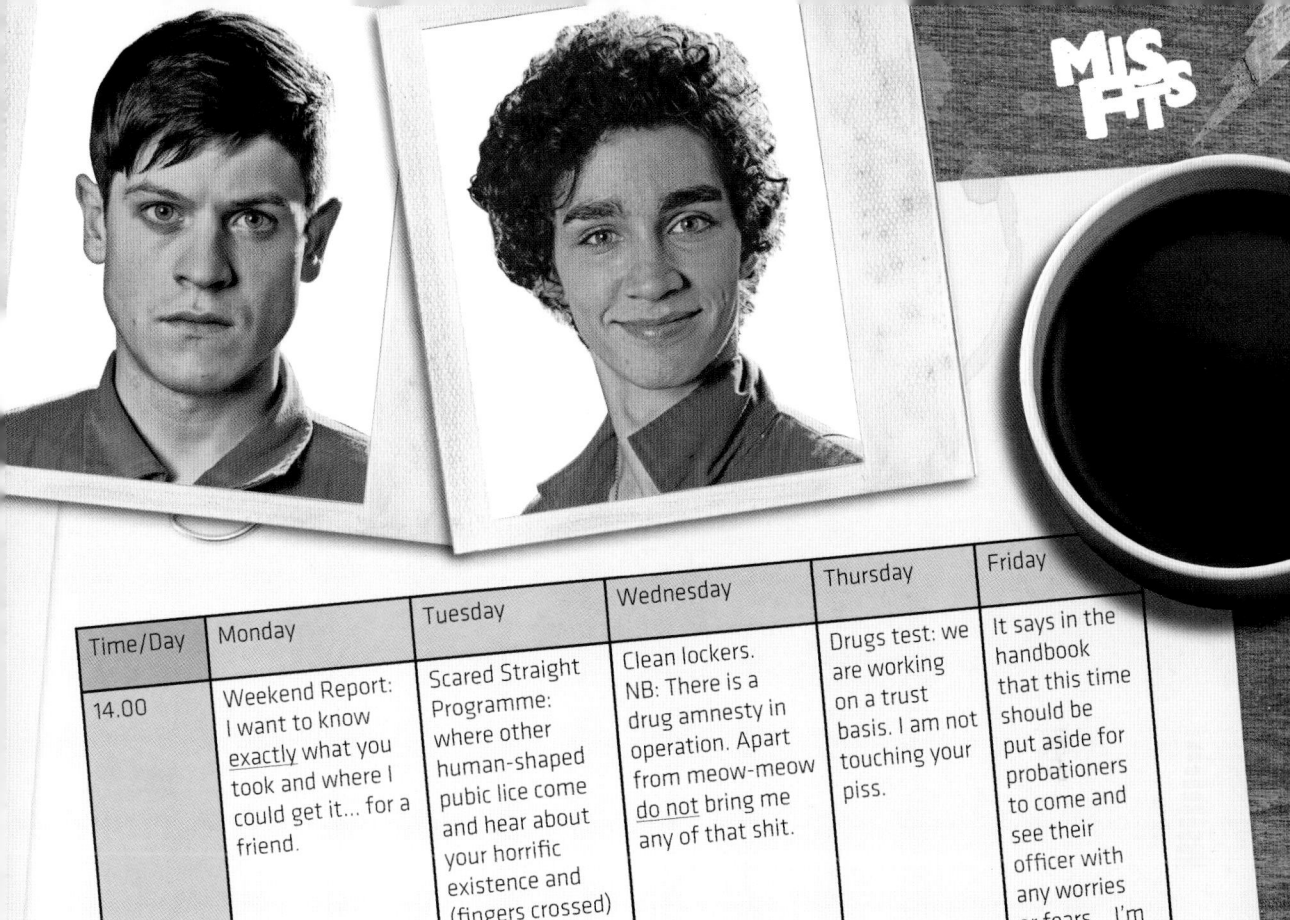

| Time/Day | Monday | Tuesday | Wednesday | Thursday | Friday |
|---|---|---|---|---|---|
| 14.00 | Weekend Report: I want to know <u>exactly</u> what you took and where I could get it... for a friend. | Scared Straight Programme: where other human-shaped pubic lice come and hear about your horrific existence and (fingers crossed) think seriously about lobotomy. | Clean lockers. NB: There is a drug amnesty in operation. Apart from meow-meow <u>do not</u> bring me any of that shit. | Drugs test: we are working on a trust basis. I am not touching your piss. | It says in the handbook that this time should be put aside for probationers to come and see their officer with any worries or fears... I'm just going to put it down as 'Quiet time'. |
| 15.00 | | | Fire drill: wait in the hall until you are <u>sure</u> I have escaped. | | |
| 16.00 | TBC: possibly personal phone-call time. | | Dead people's clothes. | Dance class. | |
| 17.00 | Helping the old. | Helping the blind. | Helping the poor. | Helping the disabled. | Helping Shaun move house. |
| 12.00 | This is your time for doing whatever it is you societal afterbirths do. I imagine it includes but is not limited to: smoking drugs, drinking meths, spurting out future degenerates, robbing the dead, telemarketing, wondering where it all went wrong, hating your parents, listening to shit music come out of your tinny mobile phone speakers on a bus with everyone secretly wanting you to choke on your gigantic, sub-human tongue etc. | | | | |

# The Agony Uncle (Part 2): Judgement Day

## It's a space for trust and sharing

**Dear Nathan,**
I have a problem. I like to go out and partake in dubstep evenings with illicit drugs involved. This in and of itself isn't a problem (I think) but the only way I can ingest said narcotics is through fizzy bumming. Am I totally messed up?

Nah, not at all. So what if you kick back with a couple of yips of a Friday evening? And so what if you're such a drug-crazed beat-fiend that you crave the rush so bad you feel compelled to squish the pills up your jacksy? What was it that your man Jesus said again? Let he who has not hoofed beans up their hoop cast the first stone. It's grand . . . we all do it.

**Dear Nathan,**
I'm seeing this guy. We get on great. Problem is he wants to get really heavy and romantic. I just want to enjoy what we have physically. Am I being unfair?

As long as you're not hurting yourself or anyone else it's fine. It's not like you've turned your rectum into a fleshy meth lab. I know this guy; total fucking oddball, needs to finger-bang his ass with MDMA just to feel alive. Which we all know is a one-way ticket to ass cancer. So next time your gentleman friend thinks you're being unfair because you're a strong, independent woman, remind him that no one's forcing him to grab a bag of blow and a pipette and head on down to brown town.

**Dear Nathan,**
I keep getting erections in the showers after football. I really don't think I'm gay but it happens every time. Is this normal?

Are you serious? Are you just new to this whole penis malarkey? Of course it's normal. I tell you what's not normal. Keeping a well-mannered romantic in your basement as your personal dick-gimp, only letting him see the light of day when you call him upstairs to fuck the dogshit out of you, slowly riding away any hint of innocence and chivalry until all that remains is a husk of a man with once virile balls that now only cough dust. But yeah, boners in showers with your buddies are par for the course.

**Dear Nathan,**
I am twenty-four years old and I've never received oral sex. I've been going out with my girlfriend for two years but she thinks it's 'icky'. This is important to me . . . but should it be?

Hey, if it's important for you, it should be important for her. You need to be honest. Like I know this guy and he fully lusts after his friends' scrotes. He should really just put his hand up and say: 'Hey guys, just to let you know I'm a member of the Brotherhood of The Head and I would hum every one of ye, take repeated loads and gargle away the taste with your balls. And while you all think we're in this private circle of macho trust, flicking each other's tight buttocks with towels, safe in the friend zone, I'm over here growing stalk. Collecting money transfers for the wank bank.' But he doesn't. Dishonest.

**Dear Nathan,**
I just found out my sister is actually my mum and I'm freaking out. Am I wrong to make it all about me?

Are you mad? Listen to me, there is no such thing as wrong. Except for when your family dumps on you that your sweet sister is actually your floozy mum and was probably getting dicked by your dad-slash-granddad. I know! Fucking scandalous. Happened to this deluded young wan. Probably didn't figure it out 'cause her eyes were so far apart on her gigantic head. Face on her like a bag of white pudding, no doubt. She was her own aunt. Imagine that. But no, what you are . . .

Oh fuck, no wait.

## GOT A PROBLEM?
Life getting you down? In a pickle? Drop me an email at Nathan@seriously-whatthefuckiswrongwith-youthatdrink-wontfix.com

# FINN'S TOP 5 TIPS
## KEEPING A SECRET

I'M NOT THAT GOOD AT KEEPING SECRETS. OR AM I? IN FACT, I'M TOTALLY SHIT AT IT. OR AM I? I PROBABLY COULDN'T HELP YOU OUT AT ALL. OR COULD I? SO HERE ARE MY TOP FIVE TIPS. OR ARE THEY? WE'LL NEVER KNOW . . .

### 1. DON'T TELL ANYONE

I know what you're thinking: it goes without saying. But does it? Does it really? 'Cause you'd be surprised how often I forget this. And it's not like I'm shit at keeping secrets. 'Cause I'm not.

### 2. TURN YOUR SECRET INTO A SOMEONE OR A SOMETHING

This always helps me. I mean, if you think about it . . . what the fuck is a secret? 'Oh, look at me, I'm a secret. Oh, no, wait. You can't look at me. Because I'm a secret.' Actually, I guess you can look at a secret. I knew this girl once called Samantha and her secret was that she had a dick and you could look at that. Oh shit, I wasn't supposed to tell anyone that.

Yeah, so turn your secret into a someone. That way it's easier to keep it in mind as a secret. Like if you always shit the bed. Call it 'Michael'. 'I'd love to stay over but Michael won't let me.' And no one will ask about 'Michael'. Because he sounds weird.

### 3. DEVELOP A SECRET FACE

Sometimes, when people are talking about stuff that's close to your secret, your face will give away that you're keeping something from them. You need to develop a secret face. A fool will tell you that this face needs to be emotionless. Guff. It needs to be in the total opposite direction. For my secret face, I roll my eyes back into my head and open my mouth in a silent scream. Job done, secret safe.

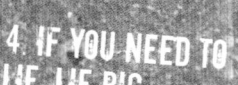

### 4. IF YOU NEED TO LIE, LIE BIG

Sometimes you need to throw out a few red herrings. A lesser secret-keeper will tell you to keep your lies little and believable. Bollocks. If you're going to keep your secret safe then you have to sacrifice your dignity. Tell them something far worse than your actual secret. Like if your dark secret is that your mum made you go to Irish dancing lessons until the age of fourteen, tell them you euthanised your own grandfather . . . and at the last moment, it looked like he changed his mind but you kept going.

### 5. KEEP TRACK OF YOUR BIG LIES

For example, never offer to mind someone's

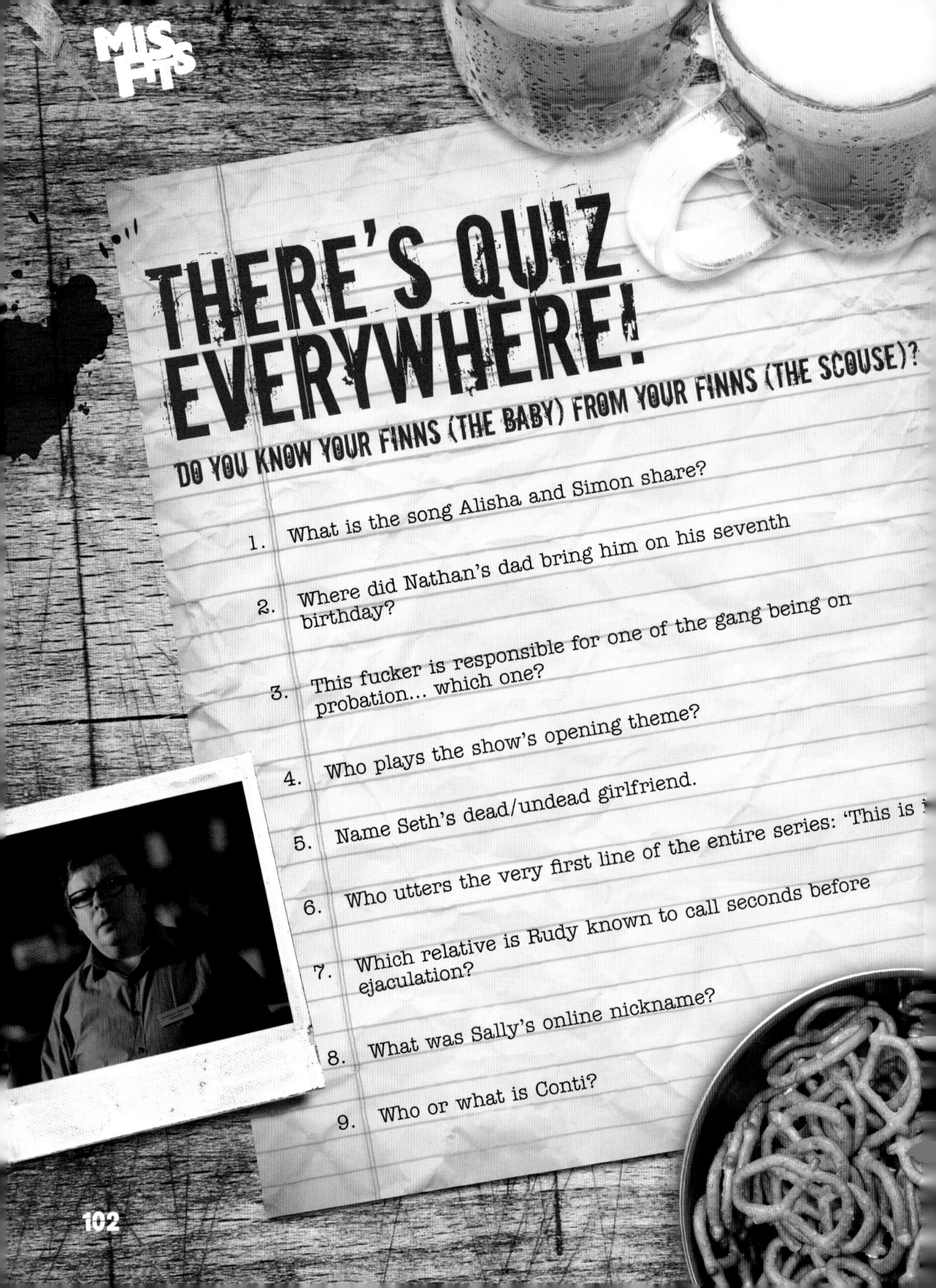

# THERE'S QUIZ EVERYWHERE!

## DO YOU KNOW YOUR FINNS (THE BABY) FROM YOUR FINNS (THE SCOUSE)?

1. What is the song Alisha and Simon share?

2. Where did Nathan's dad bring him on his seventh birthday?

3. This fucker is responsible for one of the gang being on probation... which one?

4. Who plays the show's opening theme?

5. Name Seth's dead/undead girlfriend.

6. Who utters the very first line of the entire series: 'This is i

7. Which relative is Rudy known to call seconds before ejaculation?

8. What was Sally's online nickname?

9. Who or what is Conti?

10. Which probation officer was possibly/probably abused as a child?

11. In a game of 'penis, scissors, twat' what beats 'scissors'?

12. What's the name of Kelly's dog?

13. Who does this super-strong little fella work for?

14. Where does Nathan pull a white rabbit from?

15. Who was the sixth member of the original ASBO-neers?

16. Kelly had a tattoo that she needed Vince to touch up... where is it?

17. Where was Nathan's fake girlfriend Mo-nique-ca from?

18. Who does Nikki's heart really belong to?

19. Which sweet does Nathan recommend Simon to introduce to Alisha?

20. What price does Nathan put on immortality?

21. Curtis tries to break up with Sam with a line from what movie?

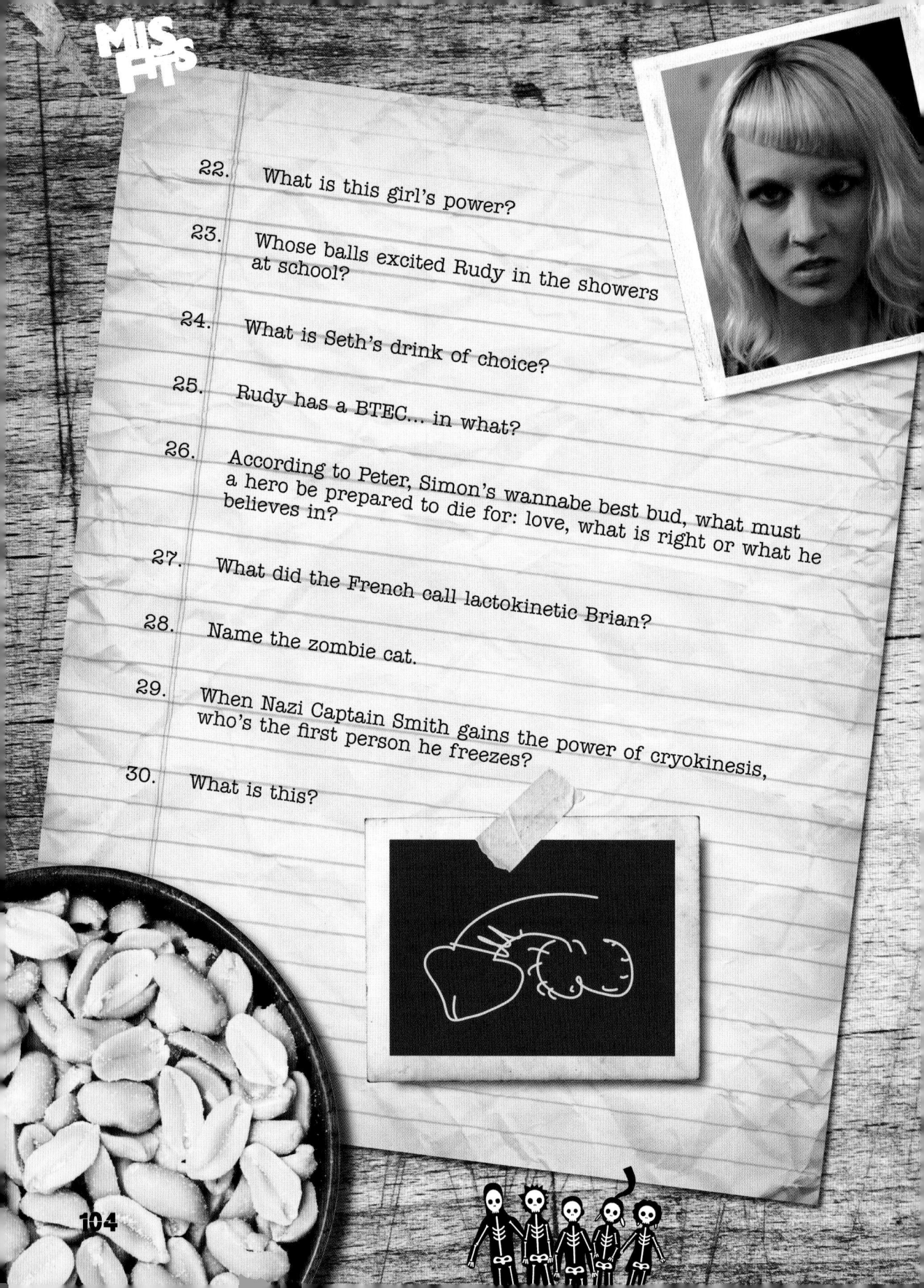

22. What is this girl's power?

23. Whose balls excited Rudy in the showers at school?

24. What is Seth's drink of choice?

25. Rudy has a BTEC... in what?

26. According to Peter, Simon's wannabe best bud, what must a hero be prepared to die for: love, what is right or what he believes in?

27. What did the French call lactokinetic Brian?

28. Name the zombie cat.

29. When Nazi Captain Smith gains the power of cryokinesis, who's the first person he freezes?

30. What is this?

## SCORES:

**0–12:** Well done. You've lived a perfect sheltered existence. Bar a couple of forays down the shop when you scuttle out like one of the monsters in *The Descent* to pick up some ramen noodles that you'll eat dry in your wardrobe, you've managed to carefully negotiate a life free from choices like 'tequila or beer?' and 'in the pink or the brown?'

**13–20:** Well done. You've hit perfect mediocrity. Some say that's average. Not me. I know hitting bland is hard to do. It's like drawing a perfect freehand circle. Only the deranged can do it.

**21–29:** Oh, nearly. But as we all know that's the same as 'nearly cumming'.

**30:** Disgusting. Seriously, I'm empty retching thinking about how much nerd there is on you. You must be covered in it. When was the last time you saw your genitals?

## ANSWERS:

1. 'The Killing Moon' by Echo & the Bunnymen.
2. Ikea.
3. Nathan.
4. The Rapture.
5. Shannon.
6. Tony the probation worker.
7. Auntie!
8. Shygirl18.
9. Conti is the boss who stole his girlfriend and £100,000 in the world of Tim the video-game guy.
10. Shaun. But don't say it to him.
11. 'Twat.'
12. Keith.
13. Seth. It's his bodyguard.
14. His arse.
15. Gary. Poor Gary.
16. On the base of her spine (tramp stamp).
17. France.
18. Ollie . . . the Greenpeace twat.
19. Fisherman's Friend.
20. Two grand.
21. Spiderman.
22. Freeze time.
23. Richard Saunders.
24. Gin and tonic.
25. Computer Science.
26. What he believes in.
27. Monsieur Grand Fromage.
28. Mister Miggles.
29. Gary. Poor Gary.
30. Rudy's severed cock.

**105**

# Rudy's Guide to SEDUCTION

I've gotten the ride. Quite a bit. I don't want to be crass so I won't put a number on it but let me say this: on average you get one STD every ten people you sleep with . . . I've had a lot of STDs. Like a ton. Loads. Here's my guide to getting you riddled.

## 1. PRE-CONVERSATION

Start confident. Make your intentions clear from the other side of the room. If you're licking out a V-sign or finger-fucking your thumb and index finger, reel it back in a bit; you've gone too far. A suggestive eyebrow will do the job. If you've raised both eyebrows, again, you've gone too far.

## 2. FINDING AN 'IN'

The hardest part (unless they're a bit rough . . . then it's the ejaculation). I find the best way is to use a bit of, you know, subliminal whatchamacallit. You want to plant the idea of riding in their heads. Has to be subtle though. Maybe hand them a condom and say: 'I'm sorry, I think you dropped this.' Suggestive eyebrow will come in handy again. And as usual if you've accidentally raised two . . . abort.

YOU AR

## 3. CONVERSATION

You want to pepper the conversation with words that have mild sexy connotations. My go-to word is 'buttload'. Coming from a guy it says: 'I really want to blow my load in your butt,' and from a gal it's basically saying: 'I love loads being blown in my butt.' So anything along the lines of: 'Ugh, I had so much work today! How much? Oh, only a buttload!' is peachy.

# 7. BROACHING THE SUBJECT OF INTERCOURSE

Broaching the subject of intercourse: Two words: genital catchphrase. You can pussyfoot around the bush all day but I think it's best to just cut to the chase. You know why you're there; they probably do too. You can skip all that political bullshit by coming up with a catchphrase to take out your genitals on. My usual is: 'You know the an . . . now gaze upon the legend!' It does the job every ne. Just off the top of my head, a good one if you're a I would be: 'They say the eyes are the gateway to the soul [take out vagina now] . . . Eeeeh-errrrr! Wrong!'

# 6. ARRIVING HOME

If you did the last point correctly, chances are your prospective porking partner will be somewhere on the scale between 'disappointed' and 'I'm so going to get raped' the minute he / she walks through your door. I like to double down and up the aunty and instantly create a sexy 'naughty' atmosphere. 'Waaaaait a minute . . . this isn't my flat. Oh my God. If we're caught we'll be in a buttload of trouble!'

# VELCOME!

# 5. THE SUGGESTION TO RETIRE

Totally depends on what time it is. As a rough guide: after bar closing – 'I got more drinks back at mine'; after chipper closing – 'I got more chips back at mine'; after club closing – 'I got more music back at mine'; after house party ending – 'I got more drugs back at mine'; after two-day bender – 'I got more tea back at mine . . . and I live with a professional psychotherapist who's also a fully qualified masseur.'

# 4. PLAYING IT COOL

Fake disinterest. 'Oh, I'm sorry. What were you saying? I didn't hear you. Why? Oh, I have a buttload on my mind.' One eyebrow.

# Wertham Probation Worker Aptitude Test

Name: ..............................................................................

Surname: .........................................................................

Date of Birth: .................................................................

Address: ..........................................................................

..............................................................................

..............................................................................

Education (if applicable): ..............................................................

Do you have any criminal convictions? If so, please give details: ..............................

..............................................................................

Answer the following yes or no questions. Circle where applicable.

Q1. Do you have any relatives? YES / NO

Q2. Friends? YES / NO

Q3. Pets? YES / NO

Q4. Basically, anyone that would miss you if you inexplicably went missing? YES / NO

Q5. Are you free from 'secret contempt'? YES / NO

Q6. Are you free from 'blatant contempt'? YES / NO

Q7. Do you want to help 'the kids'? YES / NO

Q8. Would you consider yourself a 'happy person'? YES / NO

Q9. Is this what you want to do with your life? YES / NO

Q10. Are you sure? YES / NO

If you answered 'yes' to any of the above questions the probationary service may not be for you.

PLEASE TURN OVER

If, hypothetically, you were provoked into violence by one of your wards, can you draw (hypothetically) upon this diagram where you would commit said violence?

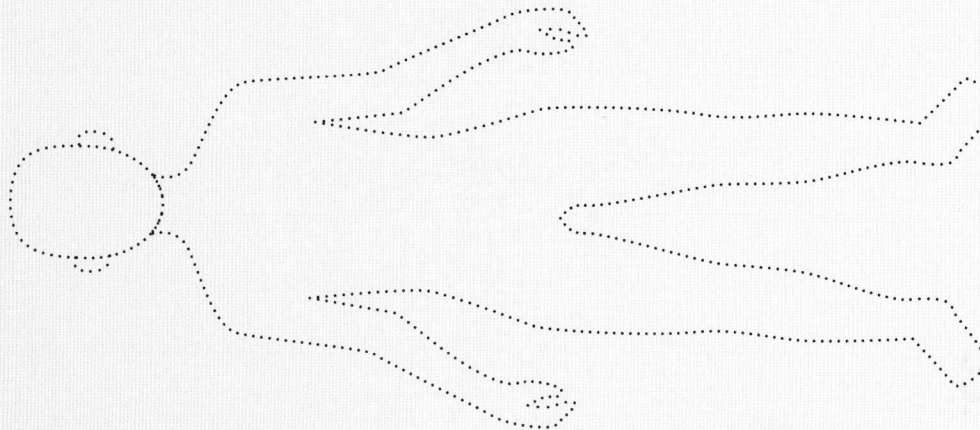

Can you draw what anger tastes like?

Why do you want to become a probation worker? ...............................................................
.................................................................

Seriously? ...............................................................
.................................................................

Okay. Brilliant. You're hired. Report to Dawn at Front Desk and she'll give you your badge.

I'm just kidding. There's no badge.

It's a laminate card.

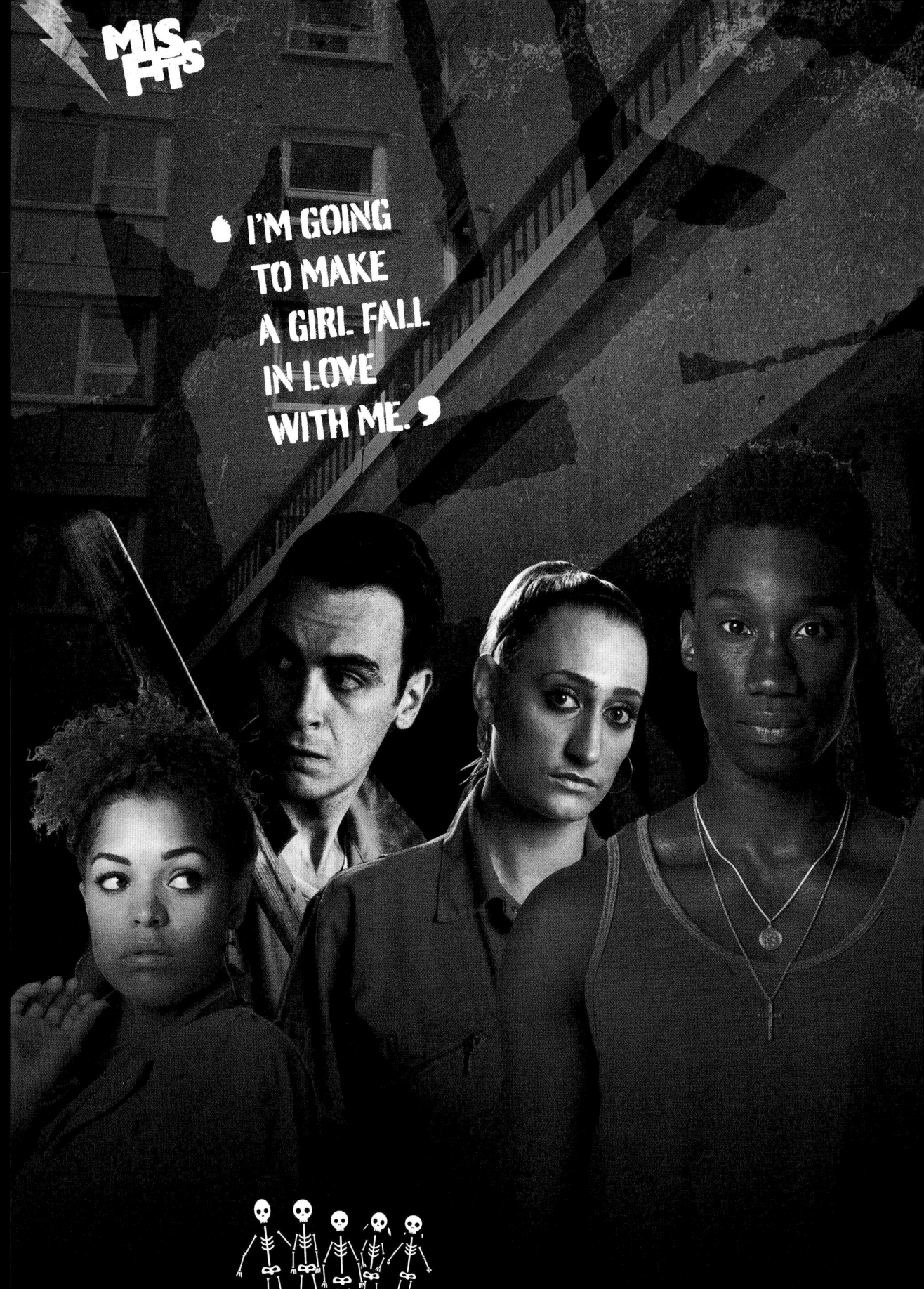

# MEET MONKEY SLUTS IN YOUR AREA

MEET SINGLE MONKEY SLUTS IN YOUR AREA. CALL NOW!
OUR GIRLS ARE WAITING ON THE LINE AND HORNY FOR YOU-OU-OU-OU-OU-AH-AH-AH-AH-AAAAAH-AAAAH-AAAAAH.

**0289 027 2785**

THIS IS BARBARA. HER HUSBAND WAS KILLED BY POACHERS FOR HIS MEAT.

AND NOW SHE'S MISSING HIS MEAT AND HUNGRY FOR SEXY CHAT.

**0289 027 2786**

HI. MY NAME IS AMY. A HOT BIOLOGIST TAUGHT ME BRITISH SIGN LANGUAGE AND NOW I HAVE NO ONE TO TALK TO.

CALL ME ON:
**0289 027 2787**

ALRIGHT? MY NAME'S MARGARET

I'VE BEEN A BAD MONKEY. THREW SHIT AT MY ZOO KEEPER. HE WON'T GIVE ME ANY BANANAS.
DO YOU HAVE A BANANA?

**0289 027 2788**

... YOU FOLLOW THE BOY AROUND THE CORNER AND WHACK! HE PLANTS HIS SKATEBOARD INTO YOUR FACE. BLOODIED, YOU FALL TO YOUR KNEES. HE THEN FORCES YOU TO DRINK A PINT OF YOUR OWN SHIT.

# MIS FITS

## Simon's Locker

HOW TO PARKOUR

**BOOK: HOW TO PARKOUR: 'I RENTED THIS FROM THE LIBRARY. IT'S COVERED IN BURGER SAUCE. SOMETHING TELLS ME THE LAST READER DIDN'T PUT IT INTO PRACTICE.'**

**PACKET OF FISHERMAN'S FRIEND: 'FISHERMAN'S FRIEND. IT'S A LOZENGE. YOU SUCK IT. FOR YOUR THROAT. AND NOTHING ELSE.'**

FISHERMAN'S FRIEND

**PAINTBALL MASK: 'IT'S A PAINTBALL MASK. FOR PAINTBALL. ONLY PAINTBALL. AND NOTHING ELSE.'**

**TOO MANY DVD BOXSETS: 'MY BOXSETS. YOU CAN BORROW ONE IF YOU WANT. ANY OF THEM APART FROM BATTLESTAR. IT'S A SPECIAL EDITION.'**

**A FLIPCAM: 'I WOULDN'T WATCH WHAT'S ON HERE. NOTHING WEIRD. I'M NOT A PERVERT.'**

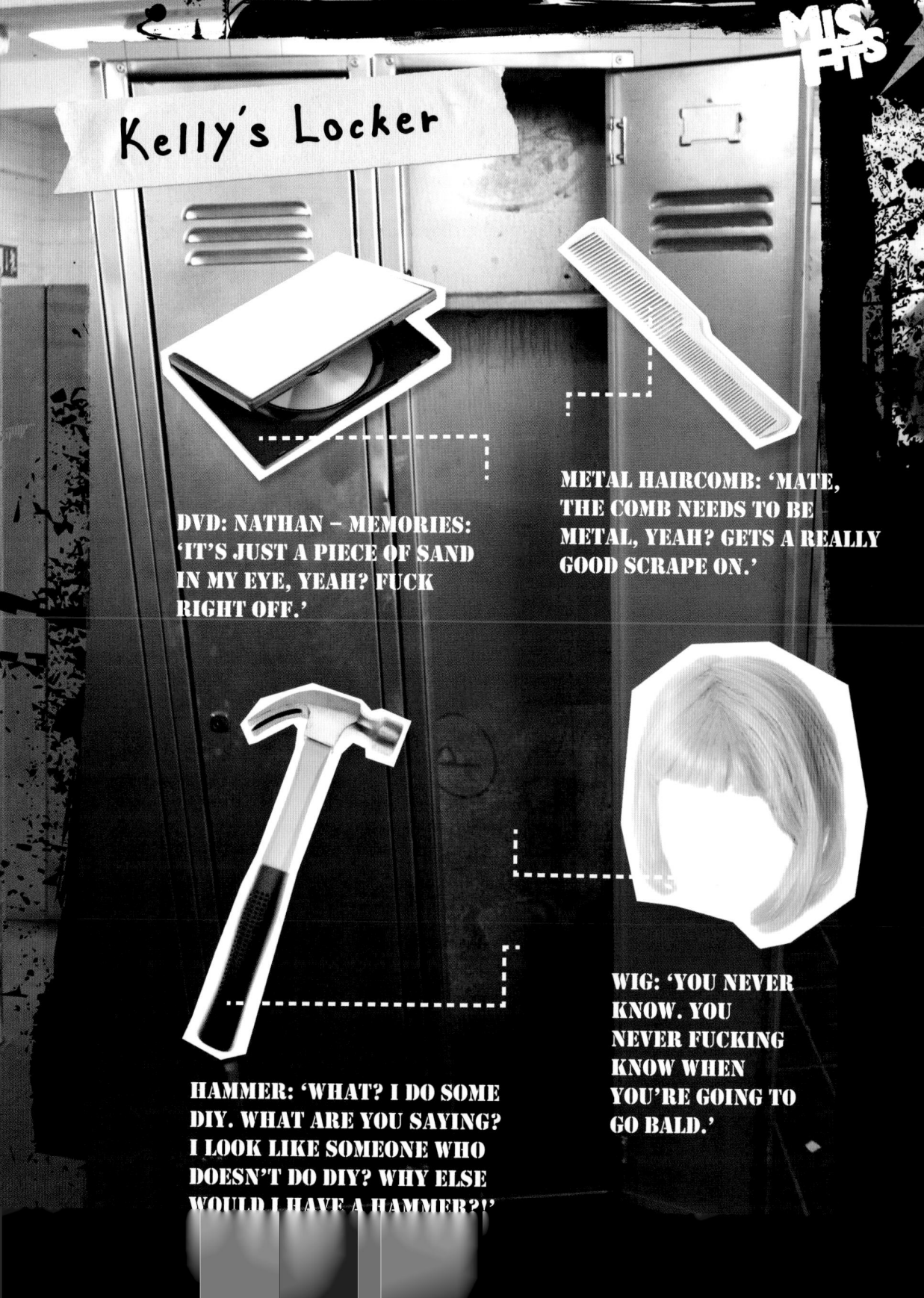

Kelly's Locker

DVD: NATHAN – MEMORIES: 'IT'S JUST A PIECE OF SAND IN MY EYE, YEAH? FUCK RIGHT OFF.'

METAL HAIRCOMB: 'MATE, THE COMB NEEDS TO BE METAL, YEAH? GETS A REALLY GOOD SCRAPE ON.'

HAMMER: 'WHAT? I DO SOME DIY. WHAT ARE YOU SAYING? I LOOK LIKE SOMEONE WHO DOESN'T DO DIY? WHY ELSE WOULD I HAVE A HAMMER?!'

WIG: 'YOU NEVER KNOW. YOU NEVER FUCKING KNOW WHEN YOU'RE GOING TO GO BALD.'

## Rudy's Locker

INDEFINABLE OBJECT: EITHER A MEDIEVAL WEAPON OR A DILDO. 'THIS? OH! IT'S, UH, A WEAPON. SELF-DEFENCE. IT'S ONE HALF OF A NUNCHUK. YEAH, THAT'S IT.'

CD: 100 GREATEST DANCEFLOOR FILLERS 'NUMBER THREE IS A CHOOOOOON. I LOVE THE BIT WHERE IT'S ALL, LIKE, NOTHING AND THEN IT GOES WOMMMPF. CLASSIC.'

100 Greatest Dancefloor Fillers.

100 Greatest Tearjerkers.

SHOVEL: 'STRANGELY PRACTICAL AROUND THESE PARTS...'

A DISCONCERTING AMOUNT OF STAINED UNDERPANTS. SOME WOMEN'S: 'UGH. THAT IS... THAT IS JUST NOT RIGHT. I HAVE NOT STOLEN THIS MANY PAIRS OF PANTS FROM WOMEN I HAVE SLEPT WITH. NO. IT'S FROM THE ONE LADY. AND SHE PUTS IT IN MY LOCKER. SHE'S A NUISANCE, A PEST.'

CD: 100 GREATEST TEARJERKERS 'NOT MINE. DON'T KNOW WHERE IT CAME FROM.  BUT I DO KNOW THIS: WHOEVER DOES OWN THIS HAS A FACE LIKE A DEFLATED SCROTUM AND HE NEEDS TO SMILE ONCE IN A WHILE.'

# Finn's Locker

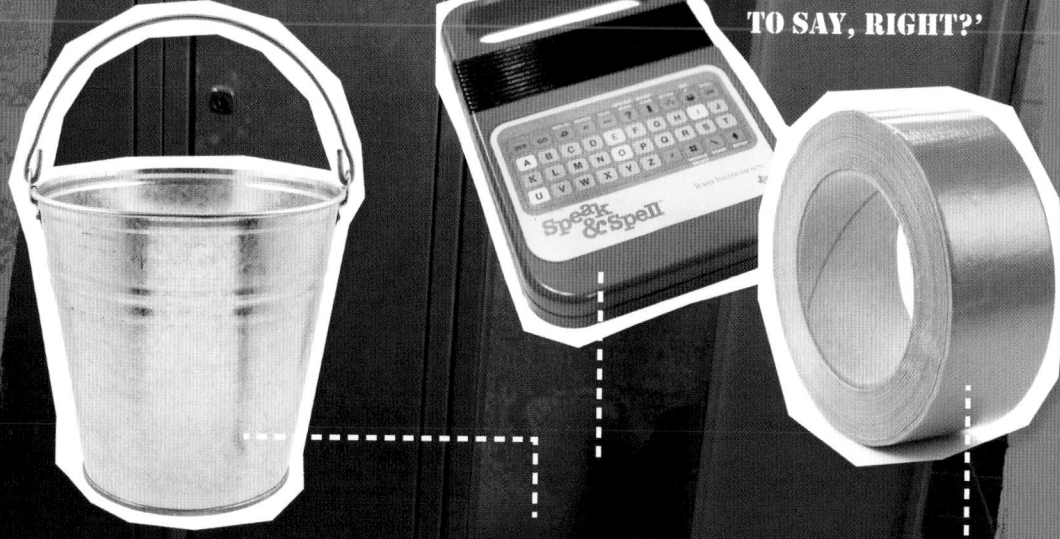

**REMOTE CONTROL FOR TV:** 'A REMOTE CONTROL IS BASICALLY A MAN'S TESTICLES. OBVIOUSLY, TESTICLES ARE A MAN'S TESTICLES. BUT THIS IS HIS OTHER TESTICLES. IN A METAPHORICAL SENSE. WHICH IS WEIRD BECAUSE IT LOOKS MORE LIKE A KNOB.'

**A PICTURE OF HIS MUM AT A PARTY:** 'THIS IS MY MUM WITH, UM, SOME FRIENDS.'

**A SPELL & SPEAK:** 'IT'S... FOR... MY DOG? THAT'S A BELIEVABLE THING TO SAY, RIGHT?'

**A BUCKET:** 'IT'S JUST A BUCKET. NOTHING WEIRD OR SINISTER ABOUT A BUCKET, IS THERE? I MEAN, I COULDN'T THINK OF ANYTHING WEIRD OR SINISTER ABOUT A BUCKET. UNLESS YOU POKED EYEHOLES IN IT AND WORE IT ON YOUR HEAD. NO. I CAN'T THINK ABOUT THAT FOR LONG. BRRR.'

**DUCT TAPE:** 'IT'S... ALSO... FOR... MY DOG? OH, NO. THAT SOUNDS WEIRD. IT'S NOT FOR MY DOG. I DON'T TIE UP MY DOG. I MEAN, I DO BUT NOT WITH SEXY DUCT TAPE. IS DUCT TAPE SEXY? I DON'T KNOW.'

# JESS'S BULLSHIT DETECTOR

Someone says something. Are they male or female?

**Female**

Who cares? It's probably true. And if it's not she probably had a good reason. Like some dickhead made her

**Male**

Are they avoiding eye contact? — **YES** → LYING! Kick them in the balls

**NO**

Are their nostrils flared? — **YES** → LYING! Kick them in the balls

**NO**

Are their hands touching their face? — **YES** → LYING! Balls kick them

**NO**

Have they lied before? — **YES** → POSSIBLY LYING. Kick their balls

**NO**

Are they good-looking? — **YES** → POSSIBLY LYING. Kick balls

**NO**

Are they drunk? — **YES** → DEFINITELY LYING! Kick balls

**NO**

Something weird is going on... Kick balls

NOT ALL OF US HAVE THE POWER OF X-RAY VISION. BUT YOU DON'T NEED IT TO SEE RIGHT THROUGH SOME PEOPLE. HERE, JESS LAYS OUT THE HOW.

DO NOT DISTURB

# Banging Your Anger-Management Counsellor

## RUDY AND RUDY TOO GUIDE YOU THROUGH THE DON'TS AND THE DO'S

*Do:* Learn to distinguish when she's wearing her 'counsellor' hat and when she's wearing her 'beautiful, intelligent, middle-aged woman who just needs some love in her life and is in no way damaged' hat.

*Don't:* Insist that she wears her counsellor hat during rutting . . . turns out, it doesn't actually exist. Fucking sham.

*Do:* Take time to listen to *her* issues when she breaks down in tears after masturbating you to completion.

*Don't:* Utter anything that could nearly, in a roundabout way, be interpreted as 'tears are the best lube'. Not even remotely.

*Do:* Realise the dangerous risk she is taking in making love with you.

*Don't:* Mess with her and pretend that you really are a dangerous risk and have a fake anger freak-out just for shits and giggles. It's not funny. I mean, it is; but pepper spray on your donger isn't.

*Do:* Walk her all the way to her house after.

*Don't:* Walk ten feet behind her all the way to her house after. See above.

*Do:* Talk about your relationship during sessions in an open and honest way.

*Don't:* Talk about your fuck sessions during group sessions in an open and honest way, always referring to her in the third person.

119

# MY DOG'S BOLLOCKS

I KNOW THIS SOUNDS RANK, YEAH? BUT SOMETIMES AFTER A BIT OF A SMOKE, YEAH? KEITH'S BOLLOCKS? REALLY REMINDS ME OF SOME SHIT. NAH, NAH, NAH. HEAR ME OUT, YEAH?

**A smaller version of Keith:**

When you really zone out on them it kind of looks like Keith is carrying a smaller Keith around under his belly. That one's the most trippy, yeah? It's like imagine if we all had a smaller version of ourselves hanging off us. I don't know if I'd like that, yeah? I'd be in relaxing and then little me on my stomach would be like all 'Get the fuck off the sofa and stop watching your dog's bollocks' . . . gobby bitch.

**A bum bag:**

This one really cracks me up. It's like he's off to a nineties rave. He's got a ton of yokes and a couple of glowsticks in there and he's just heading out the door but he's lost his keys so he's knocking about the room going, 'Have you seen my keys? Have you seen my keys?' Classic.

**An upside-down McDonald's sign:**

Yeah, yeah, I fucking know. Munchies. But come the fuck on. Even now they look like an upside down McDonald's sign and I'm totally not high. Sort of. Just a little bit, yeah? Alright, a lot.

**A pair of human bollocks:**

This has happened only once and it was the highest I'd ever been. Some fucker sold me some laced superskunk and I thought it was only weed. I rolled this huuuuuuuge bifter and I was monged out of it. When Keith walked by I thought some sicko had broken in and swapped his bollocks for Keith's.

# CURTIS' MASSIVE COCK ... TAILS

Once upon a time I was going to be running in the Olympics. Now I'm dicking around behind a bar inventing cocktails for my friends. Friends? What am I on about? Most of them are pricks.

### SIMON'S INVISIBLE NIPPLE

It's like a Slippery Nipple but you layer sambuca, vodka and gin. It's all see-through. Get it? Yeah, alright, fuck off. It's a bartender's joke, okay? Prick.

### FINN'S BABY GUINNESS

I know what you're thinking. Baby Guinness. Everyone knows a Baby Guinness. It's three-quarters of a shot of black sambuca and one quarter shot of Irish Crème and a head of cream. Standard. I don't serve Finn that. I just hand the little man a shot glass full of Guinness just to rile him. Works every time.

### RUDY'S DOUBLE

A double of anything.

(Rudy: What!? That's it! That's all I'm getting? With my shining personality that's all you can come up with? You. You are dead inside. A shell of a human being. It's disgusting. What a waste. I'm . . . I'm empty retching here. You have just come down on the wrong side of history. History will judge you, my friend. Judge you over a barrel. With no lube.)

### JESS'S BARIUM X-RAY SHOOTERS

You get a tall Slim Jim glass and you mix in a shot of gin, a shot of Goldschläger and a shot of Jaeger. Pop in an olive on a cocktail umbrella and there you have a Barium X-Ray Shooter. I call it that because if you drink it you're bound to see your guts.

### THE KELLY BAILEY'S ON ICE

Take one large glass and fill it with ice. Then pour in a good measure of Bailey's. Like Kelly *Bailey*, yeah? That's about it. Actually, Kelly thought that was a bit namby-pamby so she made me say you need to follow it with a straight-talking neat vodka chaser. Around four thumbs.

### ALISHA'S FLAMING ORGASMS

Fill half a pint glass with cava . . . 'cause she's classy like that. Then get a shot glass full of high-proof rum (it has to be high-proof). Light that on fire and drop it into the cava. Don't let the flames touch you or else you're fucked.

### THE NATHAN

Take some angostura bitters and place in the bottom of a waterproof mortar and pestle. Place one sugar-cube in and grind it until it's fully absorbed. Do the same for three more sugar-cubes. In a separate cocktail shaker, mix one part vodka, one part peach juice and one part Bacardi Breezer. Sieve through some crushed ice into a large martini glass. Then take the rind of one orange and burn it. Place the rind in the glass and pour the sugar/bitters over. Then take a cocktail umbrella . . . actually, four cocktail umbrellas and one sparkler, and decorate the glass. Finally grate some gold leaf over and there you have The Nathan.

Basically, if you order this you are a massive prick.

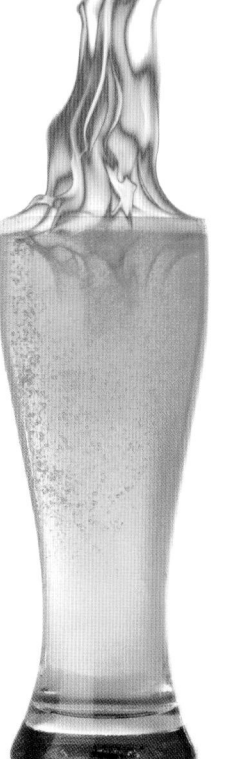

# Rudy's Rorschach

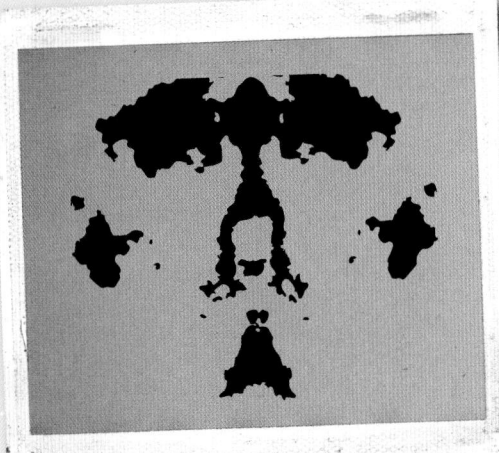

This one's obvious.

It's a turtle!

A giant bat auditioning for some type of slug X-factor. He's just hit the high-C and he's well impressed two of the judges. You can tell because he's knocked their little, tiny hats clean off. The middle slug, not so much. He's the c*nt judge.

Definitely a turtle. Is it? It is. It's a happy turtle. I mean, honestly mate, it looks seriously demented and a little bit evil. But I'm wise to your wily ways. If I say it's an angry turtle, you'll be hooking up electrodes to my nutsack before I can say 'I don't think I'm Napoleon but my wang does.' So I am going with happy turtle. Definitely not a turtle with knives. He is a turtle who has just double dropped. He's fucking loving it. Look at his little face, he's out of it. Uh-oh . . . someone needs a back rub.

Seriously?

That's sick, mate. You want to get yourself checked out. I'm actually empty retching here... huurgh. I thought these were supposed to be open to interpretation? How can anyone come up with anything other than what this clearly looks like? Is this a trick one? Is that it? You just want me to say what it blatantly is and then you'll have an excuse to shove all manner of shit up my arse in the name of science. I mean, come on. It's so obvious. It's my uncle Bernie.

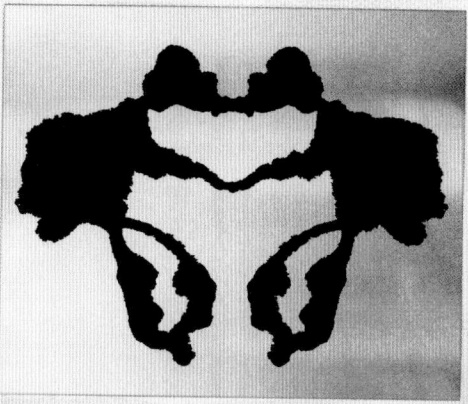

I tell you what I don't see.

I don't see two identical versions of the same fella kissing. Nope. No. It's something completely different. I'm going to go with cake. It's not two versions of me scoring the face of each other. That would be fucked up, right? What would it say about me? I'd probably be locked up. With no one for company apart from a whiney ball-bag of a bell-end. Actually, I'm going to change my answer. It's not cake. It's one person. Because there's only ever one version of any person.

Giant boner with wings.

125

## BRUNO
**Power:** Inter-Species
Transformation
**Strength:** 99
**Aggressiveness:** 99
**Aw-God-Love-'Em-Ness:** 99
**Weaknesses:** Police Brutality

## BRIAN
**Power:** Lactokinesis
**Laughabilty:** 78
**Usefulness (day-to-day):** 7
**Usefulness (murderous rampage):** 97
**Weaknesses:** Punch to the Face

## DAISY
**Power:** Healing
**Worthiness:** 85
**Usefulness (paraplegia):** 100
**Usefulness (STD):** 0
**Weaknesses:** Trophies

## FINN (BABY)
**Power:** Relationship Manipulation
**Awww Factor:** 100
**Rate of Adorbz:** 90
**Cutetagiousness:** 95
**Weaknesses:** Stable Paternal
Relationships

## FATHER ELLIOT
**Power:** Water Walking (acquired),
Telekinesis (acquired), Instant Sexual
Arousal (acquired), Teleportation (acquired)
**Strength:** 100
**Defence:** 100
**Guile:** 100
**Weaknesses:** Flying Lockers Full of Money

## LUCY
**Power:** Shapeshifting
**Machiavellianess:** 89
**Mental Wellbeing:** 6
**Weaknesses:** Realisations

# TOP TRUMPS

MIS FITS

**JODI**
Power: Alopecia Projection
Passive Aggression: 90
Taste in Men: 10
Weaknesses: Deep & Meaningfuls

**LEAH**
Power: Genital Putrification
Neediness: 90
Collarbones: 100
Traceability: 10
Weaknesses: Apologies

**JEN**
Power: Tactile Body-Swap
Dexterity: 0
Jumping ability: 0
Speed: 0
Weaknesses: Life-Support Machine

**LILY**
Power: Cryokinesis
Frostiness: 95
Desirability: 95
Chances: 1 in 20
Weaknesses: Ecstasy + Sex

127

**NIKKI**
Power: Teleportation (acquired)
Fortune: 80
Evasiveness: 65
Smoulderbility: 99
Weaknesses: Bullets

**PETER**
Power: Illustration Manipulation
Loneliness: 99
Friends: 1
Geek Prowess: 80
Weaknesses: Knives to Chest

**OLLIE**
Power: Teleportation
Ability to reason: 0
Twatability: 100
Face punchability: 90
Weaknesses: His Forehead

**RACHEL**
Power: Suggestive Hypnosis
Frigidity: 100 (latterly 22)
Followers: 99 (latterly 1)
Experience: 12 (latterly 67)
Weaknesses: Edges of High
Buildings

**RUTH**
Power: Age Regression
G.I.L.F. Factor: 96
Age: 82
But-You-Still-Wouldness: 82
Weaknesses: The Inevitable
March of Time

### SETH
**Power:** Power Transfer
**Strength:** 74
**Business Savvy:** 96
**Northernness:** 83
**Weaknesses:** Ex-Dead Girlfriends

### TANYA
**Power:** Corporeal Immobilisation
**Haircut Asymmetry:** 90
**Chip on Shoulder:** 85
**Sympathy:** 50/50
**Weaknesses:** Hard Floors

### TIM
**Power:** Psychotic Video-Game Hallucinations
**Ability to be Reasoned With:** 1
**Hatred of 'Conti':** 100
**Conscience:** 0
**Weaknesses:** Unknown

### TONY
**Power:** Berserker Rage
**Strength:** 90
**Speed:** 80
**Morality:** 0
**Weaknesses:** Fire Extinguishers

### VINCE
**Power:** Tattoo Manipulation
**Badassness:** 90
**Pomposity:** 90
**Drawing Skills:** 80
**Weaknesses:** Peanuts

**MIS FITS**

This week I'm tackling a lovely local eatery, *La Vending Machine.*

**YORKIE:** It dances on the palate, conjuring up memories of that first post-constipation shit you take three days after a music festival. Like that, but in reverse. Robust and reassuring.

**BOUNTY:** An explosion of the senses. But instead of tightly packed Semtex, it's sugary dandruff. Also makes me think of the Arctic. For some reason this is what I'd imagine munching on a husky's penis would taste like. Yeah, that's not leaving my head anytime soon.

**TWIX:** Honestly, could take it or leave it. It's not even that I mildly like it or mildly dislike it. It doesn't keep me up at night. Which is what you want from your food. Unless it's a curry.

**FLAPJACK:** This is a trick item to make you buy a drink. It's pure concentrated anti-moisture. One nugget passes your lips and your mouth becomes dryer than a desert nun's nasty bits. Needs gravy. The flapjack, not the nun.

**GENERIC WEIRD BRAND CRISPS:** Now this is a snack that really takes you on a voyage. At first you're like 'ohhh!' and then when you open them you're like 'uuuffff!' but when the smell clears a sense of 'meh' comes over you. Then you bite in. For a second you're like 'eh?' only to be sucker-punched in the kidneys by a healthy dose of 'fuck!' That's it, you think, it's game over, until 'huuuuuuuuuuuuuh' it kind of, what's the word, plateaus? Until you swallow, and the taste is punctuated with a 'BLAK!'

**CHEESE FLAVOURED CRACKERS:** Sick and wrong. Why is this in here? Why do they even make them? Yeah, they taste good together but that doesn't mean you have to make some half-cheese, half-cracker abortion of nature. It's like selling a meat-patty-flavoured burger bun. Or it's like meeting someone nice and squishing the two of you together for a bit until something pops out that's half you and half them. Bleurgh. *Wrong.*

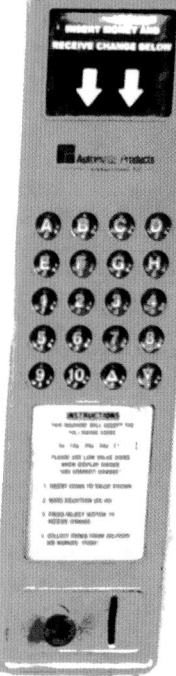

NOT A LOT OF PEOPLE KNOW THIS ABOUT ME, BUT I'M A BIT OF A FOODIE. I KNOW WHAT YOU'RE THINKING: 'FOODIE. SOUNDS LIKE RUDY. THIS IS ALL A BIT TOO MUCH OF A COINCIDENCE.' TO THE NAYSAYERS I SAY THIS: 'GET FOCCACIO'ED!' I LIKE ALL THE FLAVOURS. WELL, ALL THE FLAVOURS THAT SEVERAL YEARS OF SPEED ABUSE WILL LET ME TASTE. WHICH PRETTY MUCH WHITTLES IT DOWN TO COLD AND CHOCOLATE.

# JESS'S TOP 5 TIPS...
## ON HOW TO COMPILE A TOP 5 TIPS LIST

YEAH. HI. SO I WAS ASKED FOR A TOP FIVE LIST OF STUFF. AND WHEN I WAS THINKING ABOUT WHAT I'D DO, IT STRUCK ME HOW HARD IT IS TO COME UP WITH A TOP FIVE LIST. SO I THOUGHT I'D COME UP WITH A TOP FIVE LIST TO HELP YOU IF YOU EVER HAVE TO COME UP WITH ONE. THIS HAS NOTHING TO DO WITH ME NOT GIVING A SHIT ABOUT THIS.

### THINK OF A TOPIC YOU CAN COME UP WITH FIVE TIPS FOR.

Easier said than done. It's easy to come up with a topic. I mean, there's a load of topics in the world. Shitloads in fact. But coming up with one that doesn't make you sound like a dick is actually pretty hard. Like who wants to be the twat talking about 'music'. Fuck's sake. 'Yeah, I'm so special 'cause I like music. No one likes music. I'm a unique jewel . . .' Cock. And then would you really want to be the shitehawk talking about, I don't know, Icelandic architecture in the 1980s? It's a fine line. If you want my advice, try and come up with something on compiling a list.

### HAVE MORE THAN FOUR TIPS.

This is key. It must have MORE THAN four things on the list. So that's one . . . two . . . three . . . four . . . FIVE.

### AND LESS THAN SIX.

Crucial. If you've got to six, stop! You've gone too far.

### DON'T STICK IN ANY BULLSHIT FILLER.

I fucking hate bullshit. Timewasters can choke on a horse's dick for all I care. Honestly it gets my back up. Just fuck off.

### WHAT'S THE WORD COUNT ON THIS?
Testicles testicles testicles testicles testicles testicles testicles testicles testicles testicles testicles testicles testicles testicles testicles testicles testicles testicles testicles testicles testicles testicles testicles testicles testicles testicles testicles testicles testicles testicles testicles testicles testicles testicles testicles testicles testicles testicles testicles testicles testicles. Done.

000:00:00

II Pause

000:07:45

THIS IS EITHER THE INTRICATE PLANS OF A VIRTUOUS HERO
    ORCHESTRATING EVENTS AND MANIPULATING TIME ALL IN ORDER
FOR HIS TRUE LOVE TO RECOGNISE THE GREATNESS SLEEPING
    WITHIN HIS OLD SELF... OR THE BEDROOM WALL OF SOMEONE
MADDER THAN A BOWL OF DICKS.

# SUPERHOODIE'S WALL OF DESTINY

5 December 2011

# WERTHAM Weekly

### Making Local News Matter More

# MY PERFECT SUNDAY: Greg Adley – Local Probation Officer

I try and get out of bed before the wife wakes up. She'd like me to stay in bed all day but I just can't do it. The idea turns my stomach. I usually head downstairs and think about how I ended up here. I find it's a good way to stay focused. Then I usually make breakfast. Scrambled eggs. I find it very therapeutic. The trick to good scrambled eggs isn't to do with the butter or the cream. It's all down to your scrambling technique. I like to use a fork and zone out. I see them in the bowl, rising up. Whole bodies turn to faces and faces to eye sockets. I jab my fork into the yolk and twist until the yellow breaks and bleeds out. I grind and dig and I reach the back of the eye sockets, the metal tin of the bowl screaming against my fork. 'Stop it! Stop it!' About twenty minutes usually does it.

Then it's on to the newspapers. I know it's childish but I skip straight to the cartoons at the back. My favourite is the cat. He's so irresponsible and lazy. He has me in hysterics. What I find so funny is that his master doesn't do anything! I'd buy another cat. And then chop off its head and put it on a spike on the kitchen table just to warn him about the consequences of touching my lasagne.

Then the wife comes downstairs in her kimono so I head outside and do a bit of gardening. I haven't planted much. I just enjoy pulling out the weeds. They say you should talk to your plants, so I do. I threaten every weed just before I rip them from the earth's embrace. It's quite exhausting, coming up with new threats. But I find it very rewarding. I always carry a notebook just in case I come up with a good one I can use in the week ahead. 'I'm going to send your unborn daughter a tampon box full of your severed fingers to celebrate her first period.' I think I said that to a dandelion.

Around four, I head out for a walk in the park opposite us. There's a pond. I find ponds very soothing. Tranquil. Until the ducks come along. I hate ducks. I often think about killing them.

Back at the house and the wife has set out a traditional roast. We have a funny routine that we do most weeks. She tells me she could see me standing next to the pond and she asks me what I was laughing about and I say: 'Nothing.' Then we eat in silence. I usually think about work. I like roasts because they are an implicitly violent meal. My wife hates it when I do the screams.

After that, I go for a walk. On my own. To nowhere. Absolutely nowhere. Sometimes with my guitar. Not to play it or anything. Just to walk with it. Sometimes my wife tries to follow me but I always catch her. Those times I walk to somewhere else apa from nowhere. Nowhere is just f me. It's my time.

# A LADY'S GUIDE TO . . .

## Deciding Halfway Through a Fingering That, Yeah, You Probably Should Remain as Friends and Stop the Fingering

We've all been there haven't we, yeah? You think you like a friend. He's well funny. A bit of a dick but still. And he's alright looking. Not your usual type but still. So you say 'fuck it' and go for it. Then when you're halfway through scoring him and he drops the hand to feed the pony, an alarm goes off in your head that sounds like 'Fuuuuuuuuuuuuuuuuuuuuuck!' and you know you should have just stayed as friends. Here's how to get out of it without hurting his feelings.

FUCKING DONE.

❶ Say: 'I think we should be mates.'

❷ Make sure his feelings aren't hurt.

❸ Then say: 'You want to take that out?'

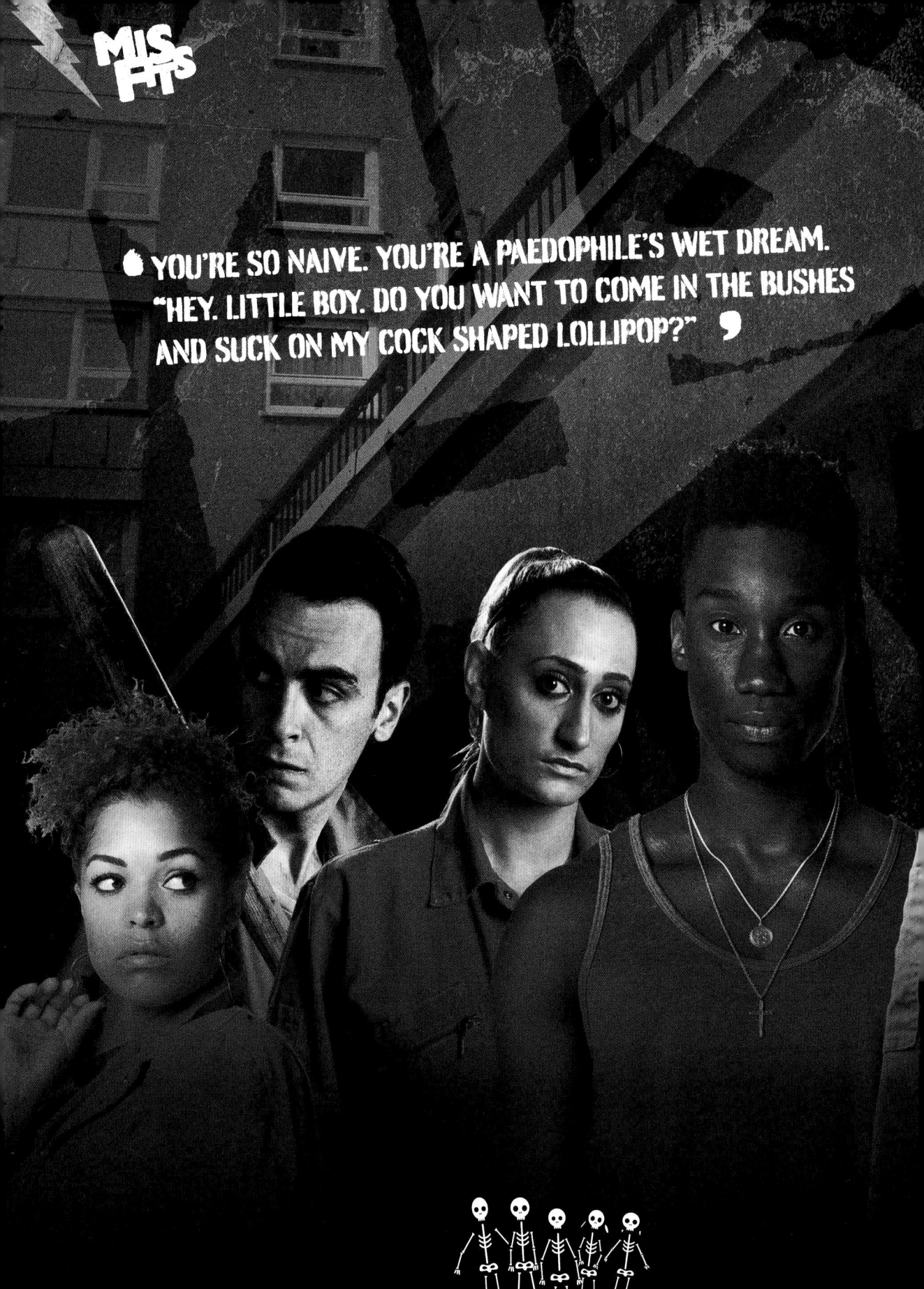

# COMMUNITY CENTRE PLAN

**Vending Machine:** It's like nature's . . . vending machine.

**Main Hall:** Mentals, old people, the blind . . . it's pretty much been an orgy of misery. But who would be the spunk-sponge at the bottom of that party? My money's on the blind. What?

**Locker Room:** This is where the magic happens. If changing clothes is your idea of magic.

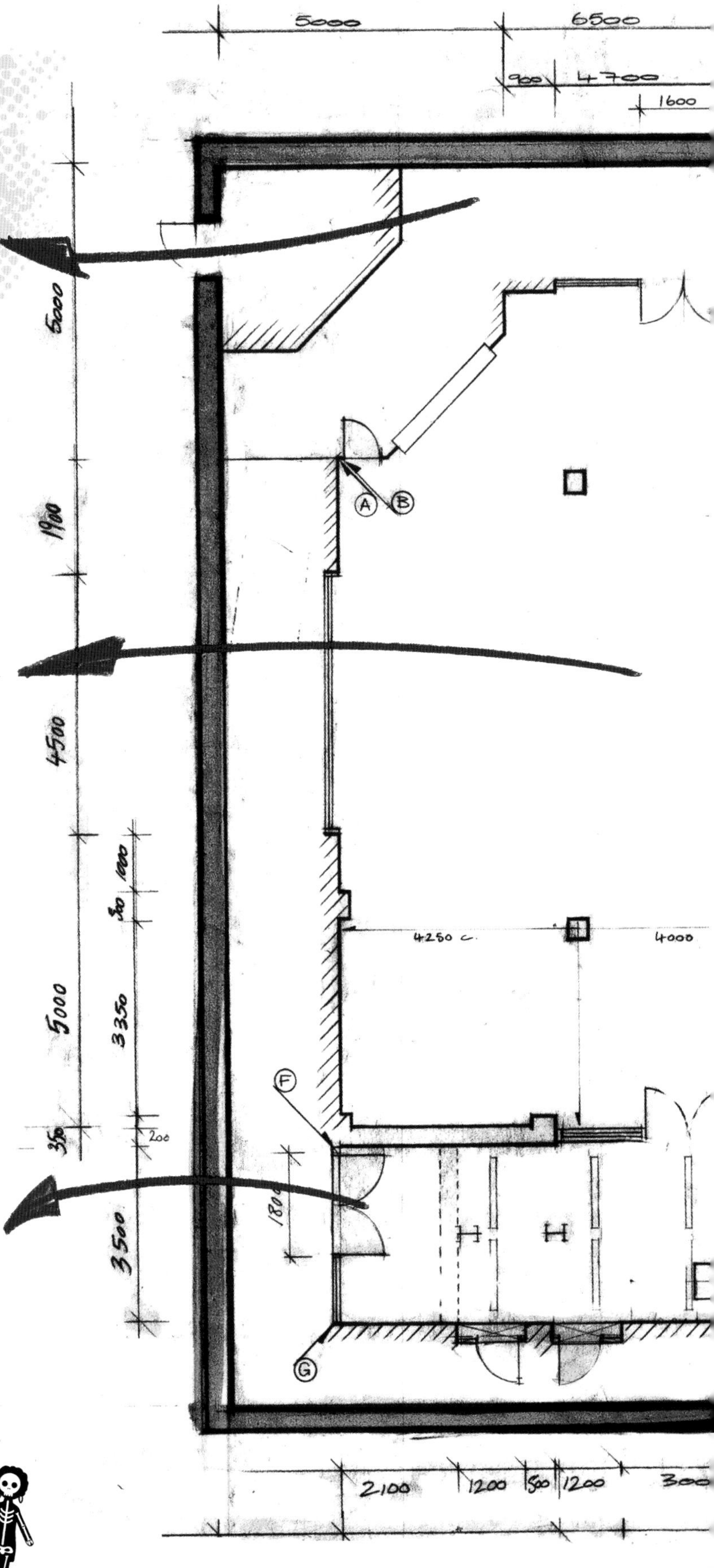

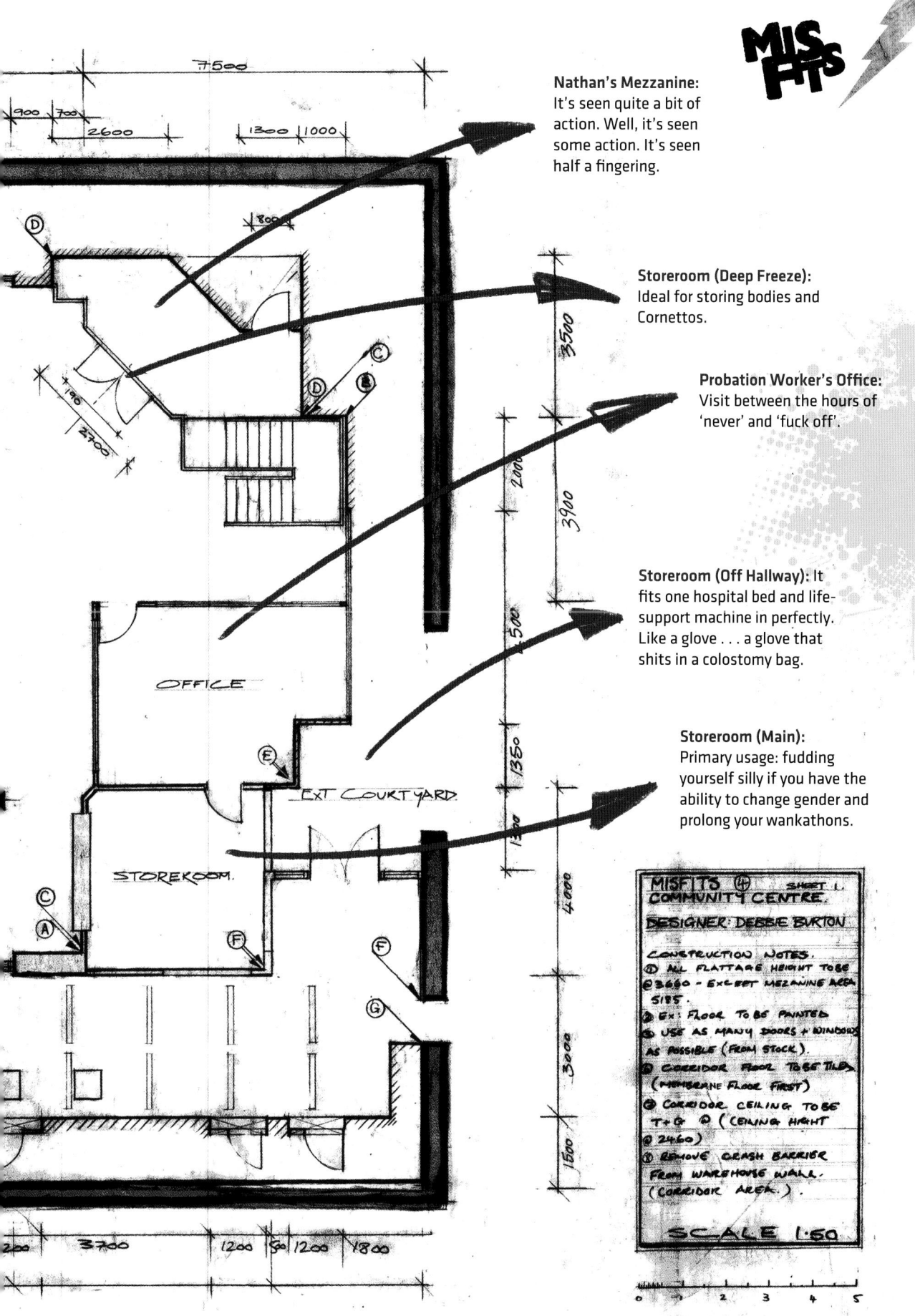

**Nathan's Mezzanine:** It's seen quite a bit of action. Well, it's seen some action. It's seen half a fingering.

**Storeroom (Deep Freeze):** Ideal for storing bodies and Cornettos.

**Probation Worker's Office:** Visit between the hours of 'never' and 'fuck off'.

**Storeroom (Off Hallway):** It fits one hospital bed and life-support machine in perfectly. Like a glove . . . a glove that shits in a colostomy bag.

**Storeroom (Main):** Primary usage: fudding yourself silly if you have the ability to change gender and prolong your wankathons.

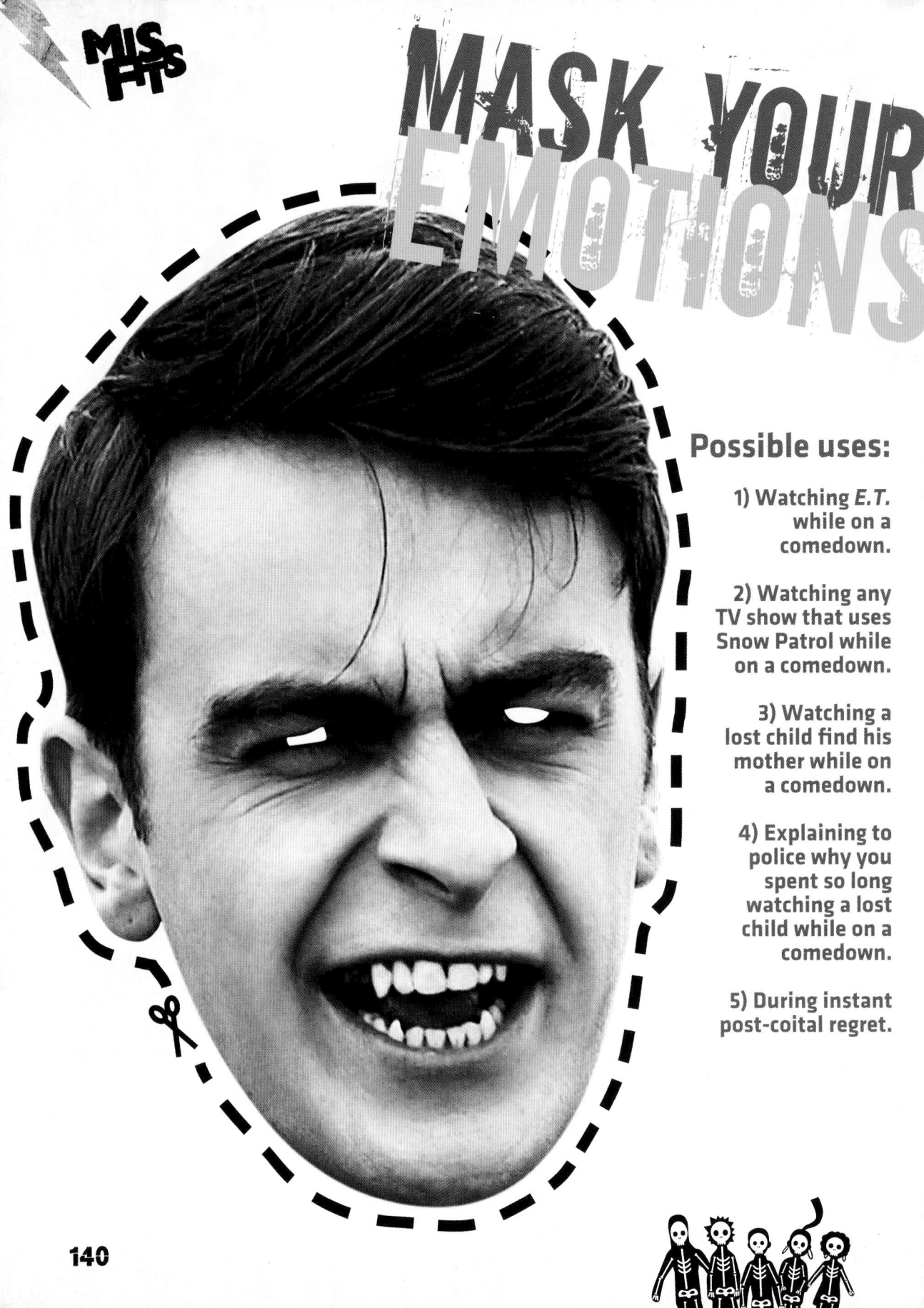

MIS FITS

# MASK YOUR EMOTIONS

## Possible uses:

1) Watching *E.T.* while on a comedown.

2) Watching any TV show that uses Snow Patrol while on a comedown.

3) Watching a lost child find his mother while on a comedown.

4) Explaining to police why you spent so long watching a lost child while on a comedown.

5) During instant post-coital regret.

REAL EMOTIONS ARE FOR THE WEAK AND INSANE. USE THESE SIMPLE CUT-OUT MASKS TO HIDE WHAT YOU'RE REALLY FEELING. IDEAL FOR POKER AND LONG-TERM RELATIONSHIPS.

## Possible uses:

1) Your gran's funeral – if she was a total bitch.

2) You're at a festival, it's two in the morning in the chai wallah tent and someone drops the 'My uncle touched me' bombshell.

3) You're at a festival, it's two in the morning in some randomer's tent and you have to play the 'My uncle touched me' card.

4) Post-bass festival break-ups.

5) Faking instant post-coital regret.

# NOTICE OF INTENTION TO APPLY FOR AN ANTI-SOCIAL BEHAVIOUR ORDER IF THE DEFENDANT IS CONVICTED AND PROPOSED APPLICATION
## (Criminal Procedure Rules 2005, Rule 50.3)

**1. THIS NOTICE** is to tell you (name and address of the defendant against whom the prosecutor intends to apply to the court for an anti-social behaviour order)

*Nathan Young (Maternal residence) Number 4, Lee Gardens, Wertham.*

**2. THE TERMS OF THE ORDER** the prosecutor wants the court to make are: The defendant must not: (prosecutor to specify here the prohibitions required)

*The defendant must attend a psychiatric assessment before commencing a community service sentence for an (as yet) undefined period of time. Sentence will be defined once defendant shuts his mouth and stops getting his sentence extended.*

**3. OFFENCE(S) WITH WHICH THE DEFENDANT IS CHARGED / HAS BEEN CONVICTED:**

*Theft of 'pick n' mix' (2 x Milky Teeth and 1 x Fizzy Cola Bottle) and causing grievous bodily harm with office equipment. Father of*

*the defendant offered compensation at scene but defendant refused.*

**4. DEFENDANT'S STATEMENT:**

*What is wrong with the world if a young ragamuffin such as myself can't help himself to one or two little sweeties for being a good boy. The snaffling of pick n' mix is enshrined in the constitution, no? I can explain the stapler thing. I thought Beverly was going to touch me. On my winkie.*

**5. VICTIM'S STATEMENT:**

*He needs to be locked up. He's an animal. A savage. Went bloody mental on the lanes so he did. And I wanted to help him. I really did. But he doesn't want people's help. He just wants their hard-earned pick n' mix. Comes from a broken home, you know?*

## METROPOLITAN POLICE

### POLICE INTERVIEW TRANSCRIPT

**DCI C:** Interview starts at 23.20. This is DCI Steve-

**NY:** Interview starts at 23.21. This is Detective Nathan Young-

**DCI C:** What are you doing?

**NY:** I'm the one asking the questions here, Bertie Big-Balls.

**DCI C:** Sit down!

**NY:** You sit down.

**DCI C:** I am sitting down.

**NY:** See? I'm the one calling the shots.

**DCI C:** Do I need to stress the seriousness of your crime?

**NY:** (Mumbles)

**DCI C:** Excuse me?

**NY:** I SAID I WANT YOU OFF THE CASE!
[Silence]

**DCI C:** Interview starts at 23.23.

# KELLY'S TELEPATHY TEST

## IT'S ACTUALLY A LOT EASIER THAN YOU'D THINK, YEAH? PIECE OF PISS, REALLY.

**So you know when you're off your box and you're dancing to this tune and the tune is one of your favourites, yeah?** But because you're off your box, it's better than banging. It's like new banging, yeah? You fucking love this song, even listened to it just before you left your house. But then, yeah? You pick out this tiny cymbal, yeah? It's been there all along but you never heard it until now. And now it's all you can hear. 'Cause you're off your chops. That's what mind reading is like, yeah?

So, like, pretend you're off your chops and think about me as that tune. Now, zone out, yeah? G'wan. Yeah? You zoned? Now, I'm thinking of one of these cards and that's the tiny little cymbal yoke. Are you getting it?

**Pick one.**

Now turn the page to find out if you're telepathic.

143

Jog on,
knob-head.

# COURT ORDERED ESSAYS

DEAR SHITBAGS,
WHERE ARE THOSE COURT-ORDERED ESSAYS I ASKED FOR? OR DO I HAVE TO GET VIOLENT? I DON'T MIND. I LIKE GETTING VIOLENT. THE ONLY PROBLEM IS I HATE STOPPING BEING VIOLENT. YOUR CHOICE.

Rudy

What have I learned on my time on probation? There is actually only one way to skin a cat. Hang on, hang on. I know what you're thinking, 'But Rudy, that's not the saying! How can you be so blessed in the pants department and so lacking in the brains arena?' Well, to that I say my brain is in my pants department. But not in a bad way. In a brainy bollock way. Am I making sense? Back to the cat. Okay. So one way to skin the cat. Technically there are many ways, but in the end you have a cat and then you skin it and then you have a cat with no skin. And a big pile of cat skin. We can't ignore that. But let's put it to the side for the moment and focus on the cat. There is a cat, it had skin, now there is no skin. Alright. Are you still with me? Okay, good. So, the way the cat got skinned was that it had skin and then the skin got removed. That is the way it got skinned. You see? It doesn't really matter how you skin the cat because all the cat is thinking is, 'Fucking hell! I just got skinned!' You know? Do you see? All this, everything, it's just different ways of doing the same thing. We're all just doing the same thing. But we think we're doing different things. But I know. I'm like the cat. I know I just got skinned. I can also see that the little fat emperor fella is naked. He's naked and I'm a cat. And he has my skin. And we're drinking pints. That is what I have learned.

**145**

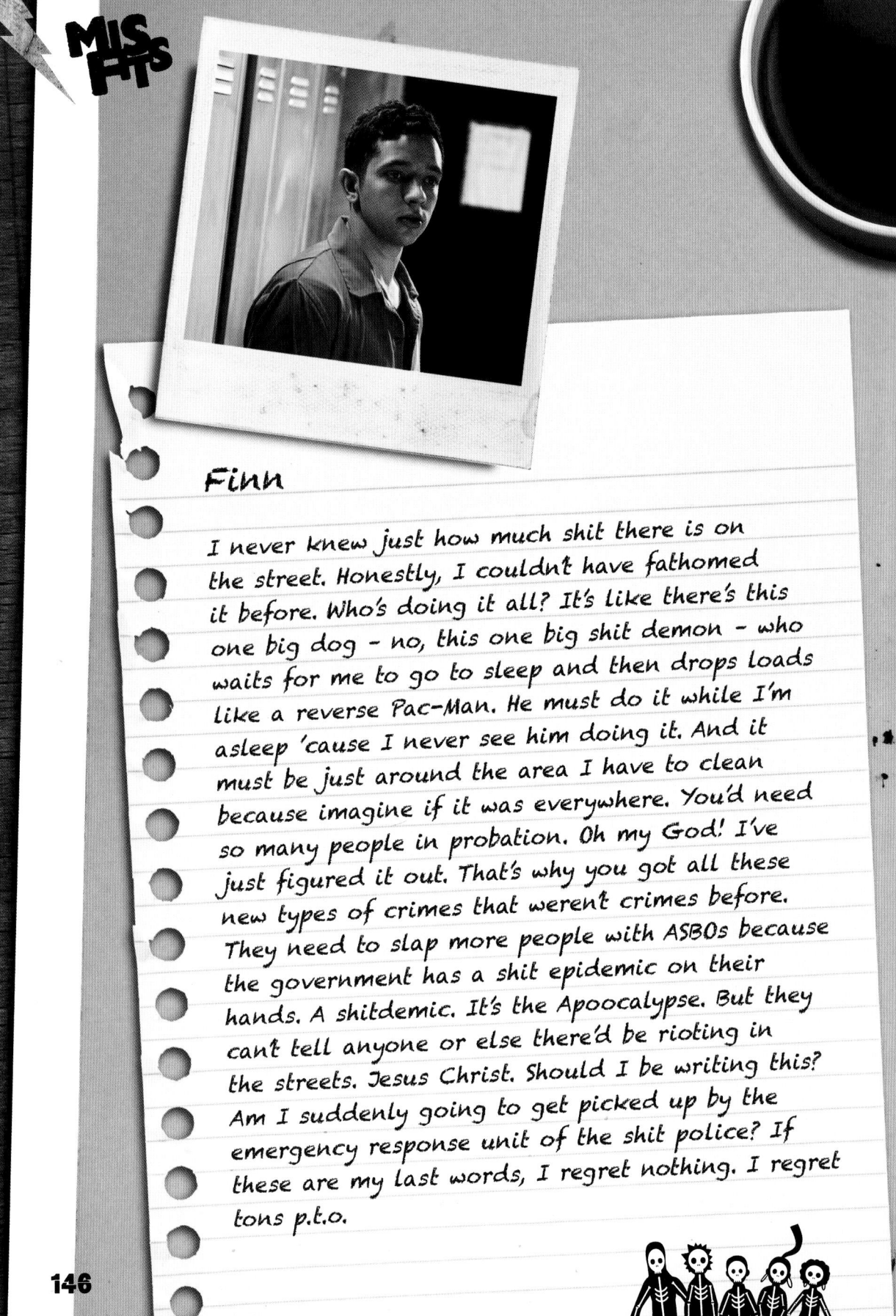

## Finn

I never knew just how much shit there is on the street. Honestly, I couldn't have fathomed it before. Who's doing it all? It's like there's this one big dog – no, this one big shit demon – who waits for me to go to sleep and then drops loads like a reverse Pac-Man. He must do it while I'm asleep 'cause I never see him doing it. And it must be just around the area I have to clean because imagine if it was everywhere. You'd need so many people in probation. Oh my God! I've just figured it out. That's why you got all these new types of crimes that weren't crimes before. They need to slap more people with ASBOs because the government has a shit epidemic on their hands. A shitdemic. It's the Apocalypse. But they can't tell anyone or else there'd be rioting in the streets. Jesus Christ. Should I be writing this? Am I suddenly going to get picked up by the emergency response unit of the shit police? If these are my last words, I regret nothing. I regret tons p.t.o.

## Jess

Don't get caught.

How long does this have to be? 500 words???? Testicles testicles testicles testicles testicles testicles testicles testicles testicles testicles testicles testicles testicles testicles testicles testicles testicles testicles testicles testicles testicles testicles testicles testicles testicles testicles testicles testicles testicles testicles testicles testicles testicles testicles testicles testicles testicles testicles testicles testicles testicles testicles testicles testicles testicles testicles testicles testicles testicles testicles testicles testicles testicles testicles testicles testicles testicles testicles testicles testicles testicles testicles testicles testicles testicles testicles testicles testicles testicles testicles testicles testicles testicles testicles testicles testicles testicles testicles testicles testicles testicles testicles testicles testicles testicles testicles testicles testicles testicles testicles testicles testicles testicles testicles testicles testicles testicles testicles testicles testicles testicles testicles testicles testicles testicles testicles testicles testicles testicles testicles testicles testicles testicles testicles testicles testicles testicles testicles testicles testicles testicles testicles testicles testicles testicles testicles testicles testicles testicles testicles testicles testicles testicles testicles testicles testicles testicles testicles testicles testicles testicles testicles testicles testicles testicles testicles testicles testicles testicles testicles testicles testicles. testicles testicles testicles testicles testicles testicles testicles testicles testicles

# BALD KELLY

## A WIG FOR EVERY OCCASION

### Wig Examples:

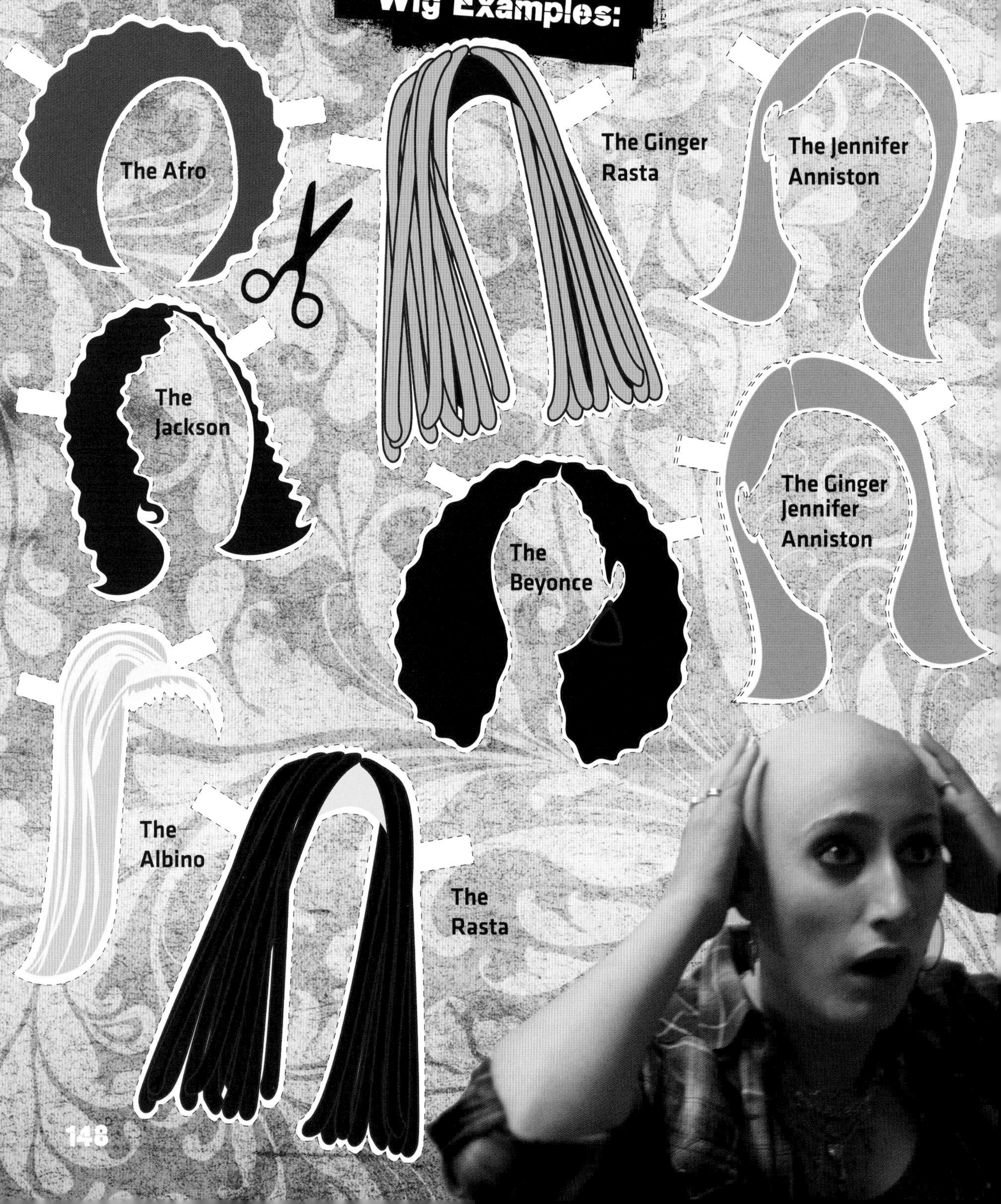

The Afro

The Ginger Rasta

The Jennifer Anniston

The Jackson

The Ginger Jennifer Anniston

The Beyonce

The Albino

The Rasta

# Curtis's Top 5 Tips For...
# Putting up with Pricks

Only two things in life are certain: death and having to put up with pricks. The world is full of them and the sooner you realise you're never going to escape curly-haired fuckwads who shit in beds first and ask questions later, the better.

## 1. The Documentary Crew Technique

What helps sometimes is pretending there's an invisible documentary crew in the room. When some prick says some prickish thing, look to the camera and mouth, 'Oh my fucking God.' That signals to the people watching that you're actually outside the circle of pricks. Okay, yeah, they're imaginary people but imaginary people need to know you're not a prick too.

## 2. The Carer Technique

I use this when I have to walk around with a bunch of pricks. Imagine, in your head, that you're their 'carer'. Alright, no one will actually think that that's the case but fuck them. They're probably pricks anyway.

## 3. The Mountain Gorilla Technique

When a prick insists on talking to you, pretend they're a mountain gorilla. Drop your head and avoid eye contact until they stop talking and go away. I like this one 'cause: 1) you feel like there's a bit of adventure in your life and 2) the prick fucks off.

## 4. The Finger Tweet Technique

A bit like number one; when a prick comes out with some prick statement, retweet it with an imaginary phone. I don't know why this helps but it does. It works really well if you steal the prick's imaginary phone to do it on. Hahahaha . . . stupid prick.

## 5. The Abuse Technique

All pricks are pricks for a reason. Probably some form of fucked-up abuse.
It helps if you picture it.

# SIMON'S Bottom 10 Superheroes

**1**

**2**

**3**

**CAPTAIN BOOMERANG,** aka George 'Digger' Harkness, was originally an enemy of the Flash. He dedicated himself to battle his superhuman sonic speed with . . . a load of boomerangs. He died.

**ARM FALL OFF BOY,** Floyd Belkin of the planet Lallor has the ability to detach his arms and use them as blunt instruments to club his enemies. I can't imagine what type of enemies he would have.

**EXTRAÑO.** I'm not making this up. Extraño (Spanish for 'odd' or 'strange') was probably the first openly gay comic book hero. He used to refer to himself as 'Auntie' and wore the most flamboyant costume in tights-wearing history. In one mission, Extraño was attacked by the 'AIDS vampire' Hemo-Goblin and contracted HIV. I'm not making this up.

**7**

**MATTER-EATER LAD.** Matter-Eater Lad's superpower was that he had the ability to eat any type of matter. What type of matter? It didn't matter, Matter-Eater Lad would eat it. It was handy for getting out of jails and . . . yup.

**8**

**HINDSIGHT LAD.** Carlton LaFroyge didn't have a special power. He did have 20 / 20 hindsight though. And a caped costume that included side mirrors from a car attached to an American football helmet.

**4**

**STILTMAN.** Uh . . . he has stilts.

**5**

**SQUIRREL GIRL.** First appearing in *Iron Man*, Squirrel Girl, aka Doreen Green, has superhuman squirrel-like abilities and can communicate with squirrels. She also has a tail. I know this is supposed to be a worst-of list but she actually defeated Doctor Doom once, overrunning him with squirrels, causing Doom to exclaim: 'Confound these wretched rodents! For every one I fling away, a dozen more vex me!'

**6**

**TEN-EYED MAN.** Philip Reardon lost his sight due to a war injury received in Vietnam. A mad scientist implanted optic nerves on the tips of his fingers. Which is perfect for fighting superpowered foes . . . unless you have to make a fist.

**9**

**DOGWELDER.** Appearing in the *Hitman* series, Dogwelder was a superhero who welded dead dogs to evildoers, to terrify and maim them. I'm sure it's a metaphor for something. I'm just not sure what.

**10**

**THE RED BEE** By day Rick Raleigh is an assistant district attorney. By night he dons a costume and fights crime as The Red Bee. How does he fight crime? He has a gun. And a trained bee called Michael that he keeps in his belt buckle. He got killed by a Nazi. Rick did. I'm not sure what happened to Michael.

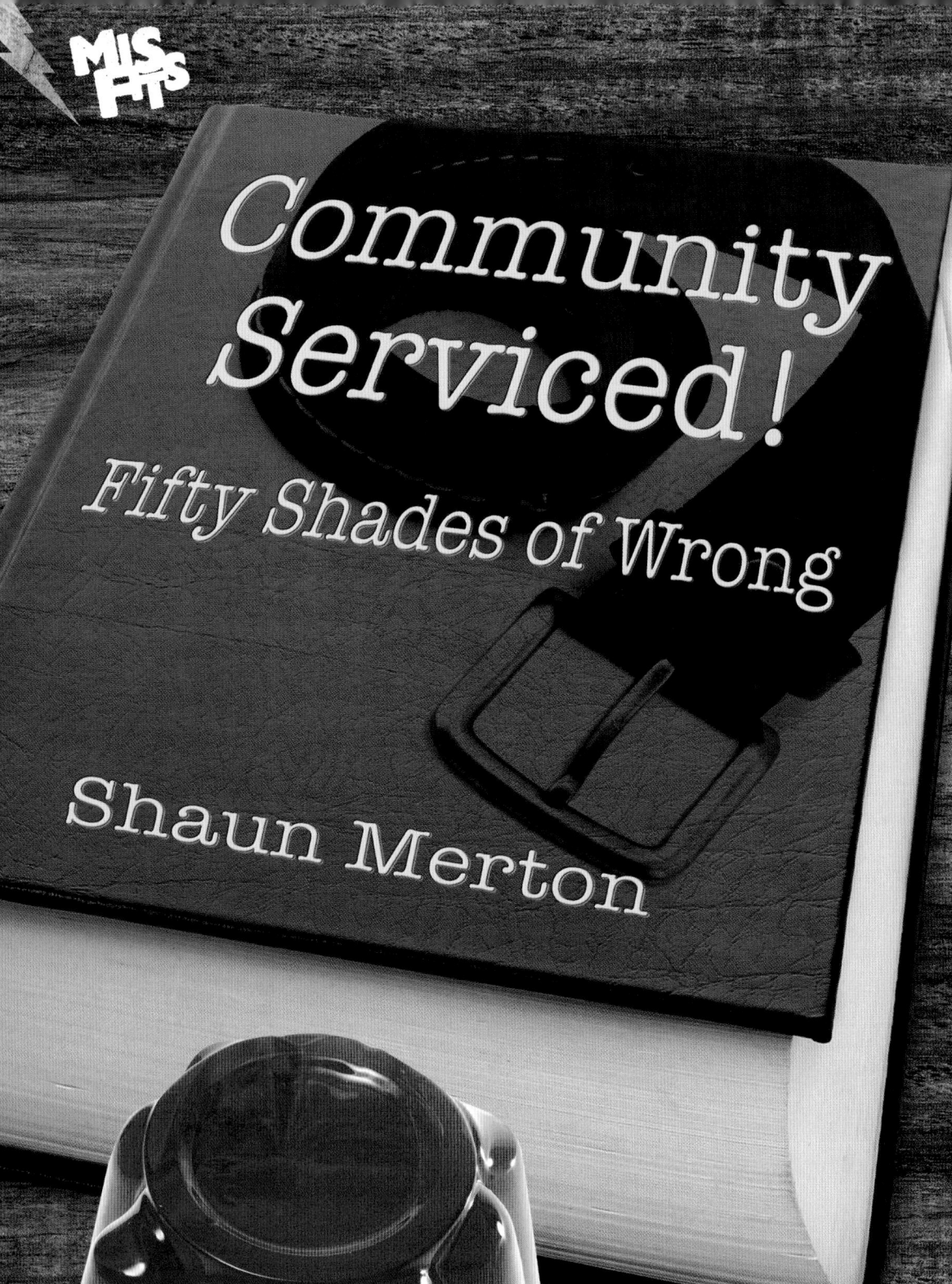

# Community Serviced!

## Fifty Shades of Wrong

### Shaun Merton

# Shaun's Erotic Novel

Title: Community: Serviced!

Sub-title: Something's up with your email, I think I'm getting marked as spam. Thought it'd be best to send the latest draft in the post (registered). My latest draft is quality. It's going to make us a brick load of cash. And since I actually work in the service all the fatties on *Loose Women* will eat that shit up. Om om om. Get back to me with your thoughts (i.e. 'Shaun, you are a fucking genius').
Regards,
Shaun

Copy

'How are those disgusting old people going to eat all this jelly?' thought Malisha as she stirred the inflatable pool. Which was full. Of jelly. She sighed and looked around her prison… the community centre. Was this really the centre of the community? Little did she know this hall was about to become an amphitheatre of amorous athletics…

Malisha was an exquisitely beautiful woman with ample proportions. So ample were her proportions that she had received much attention from the male of the sexes throughout her young life, which was, in part, thanks to her proportions. Which were ample. She wiped her brow and gazed inquisitively over to her fellow ASBO amorous companion. Nelly was a terrifying vixen who would knife you in a second if you didn't agree to load your love-muscle into her if she so demanded… but you definitely would.

The two girls were here because they had been very bad girls. Very bad girls indeed. They were here to learn a lesson. Little did the law know that that lesson was soon to be… Man.

Nelly said something that was unintelligible. 'I know' said Malisha breathily, 'I can't believe we have to work in candlelight. But it serves us right. The Master said we do not deserve to work like human ladies yet and that he would beat us with his leather belt again if he caught us using electricity and I don't want that'. 'Or do I?' she thought. And looking over at Nelly bending low in the flickering candlelight she could see his point. She didn't look quite human. More like a creature that should be used exclusively for love-making.

Whilst her mind was momentarily departed on some male-member-infused reverie she felt a soothing cold splat hit her breast. Unfortunately, it wasn't man sauce. It was jelly that Nelly had thrown playfully at her. A coy smile spread across her face like man sauce across a buttock and she picked up a globule of the pink mess and threw it back at Nelly. Nelly said something unintelligible and launched herself across the pool at Malisha, dragging her in, two bodies enmeshed and writhing in the heap of lube food. Slipping, sliding, briefly touching each other's sex for the briefest of brief moments. 'Oh' said Malisha. Nelly said something unintelligible.

'What is this I see before me?!' a loud voice bellowed across the hall, the aural vibrations reverberating deep into each girl's love cleft, setting a thousand synapses alight in that part of their brains responsible for the most deadliest of sins… lust.

It was The Master.

'It was an accident' whimpered Malisha, doing a half-hearted job of hiding her excitement. Nelly said something unintelligible.

'It didn't look like an accident.' The Master spoke, 'It looks like you two have been up to your old tricks. Tricks that require…' The girls bit their lips in expectation, '… a punishment.'

PTO

# BEGINNER'S GUIDE TO PARKOUR

**SIMON:** The idea behind Parkour is getting from point A to point B in the fastest time possible. Which is useful when you have to be on time. Especially to prevent things that must not come to pass. And making things happen that have to. Don't worry. It'll all become clear . . . soon.

It's also good for catching the bus.

Parkour is not easy . . . but if I can do it, you definitely can. Here are some simple moves to get you started.

## PRECISION JUMP

This move is for jumping from one obstacle to another, landing on your two feet. The jump is usually performed from a standstill position. It is important that you land on the balls of your feet with your feet together and 'stick' the jump. This means don't fall forward or backwards off whatever you just landed on. It's called the Precision Jump as you have to land precisely rather than the usual roll. Which brings us on to . . .

## TIC TAC

This move allows you to spring off a vertical wall and over a medium fence below. As you approach, take in a deep breath through your nose. Bring one leg up to the surface you are performing the Tic Tac off of. Let out the breath through your mouth in a powerful 'shu' as you pounce off of the object. Twist your body out and upwards. Throw your arms in the direction you are landing. Land.

## MONKEY VAULT

This move is used for vaulting over mid-sized obstacles like walls or cars or wheelie bins. Run straight towards the obstacle. Then (at speed) place both hands on the top of the obstacle. Pull both legs up in a squat position with the hips raised and pull yourself through your arms and over the obstacle.

## PARKOUR ROLLS

## CAT LEAP

The most important Parkour move to learn, it lightens the impact of your fall or landing when jumping from high obstacles. The trick is to land on the balls of your feet and let your momentum naturally carry you into a roll. Before you land, have your hands out in front of you; it helps to hold them in a diamond shape. When you land tuck your chin in, use your hands to carry you forward into a roll onto your shoulder and diagonally across your body, down to your, um, arse. Now roll up onto one leg and use the momentum to propel you forward.

Basically, land and do a roll.

I use the Cat Leap when an obstacle is too high to jump. And especially if there's a high gap between me and the obstacle. Run at the top of a wall. Jump and, once airborne, you should partially extend your legs towards the wall. Absorb the impact with your legs first, bending your knees and landing on the balls of your feet. When your feet touch the wall, grab the top of the wall with your hands. Then you can drop down, jump to another wall, or scurry on top of or over the current wall.

NATHAN: Parkour is not cool. On the ladder of cool it's just a notch below 'Rolf Harris' and a smidgen above 'being born with an actual mouse's fanny'. Totally not cool. Even if you try and make it sound cool by being all vague and weird. 'Parkour is good for when the wind blows between the cuckoo's dusty scrotum.' See? Still not cool.

Here are some moves to help you make it cool.

## THE DALAI LAMA

This technique should only be used when tackling large walls. Run towards the wall. Then climb up the wall. Stand on top of the wall. And give people passing underneath the wall the finger. With both hands. Maybe shout something like 'Here! You! You big bollocks!' When bored climb back down off the wall.

## THE GRACEFUL NERD

This move is a traditional Parkour move, in that it gets you from point A to point B in the shittest way possible. Start a steady stride towards the bonnet of a car. When you reach the car slide like a gimp onto your back on the bonnet of the car. Wriggle around a bit, repeatedly shouting 'Parkour! Parkour!' then go limp and slide off the edge into a heap on the ground.

MIS FITS

Every bride deserves one.

Drive him insane at the altar in one of this season's new bridal gowns.

Drop in to us at 'Let's Frock!' for a free fitting.

A Special Day

# NOTICE OF INTENTION TO APPLY FOR AN ANTI-SOCIAL BEHAVIOUR ORDER IF THE DEFENDANT IS CONVICTED AND PROPOSED APPLICATION
## (Criminal Procedure Rules 2005, Rule 50.3)

**1. THIS NOTICE** is to tell you (name and address of the defendant against whom the prosecutor intends to apply to the court for an anti-social behaviour order)

Rudy Wade, Flat 7, Beechdale, Beaumont Avenue, Wertham.

**2. THE TERMS OF THE ORDER** the prosecutor wants the court to make are: The defendant must not: (prosecutor to specify here the prohibitions required)

The defendant must complete a community service order, attending a payback scheme. He must also report to an assigned counsellor for anger-management sessions.

**3. OFFENCE(S) WITH WHICH THE DEFENDANT IS CHARGED / HAS BEEN CONVICTED:**

Destruction of property (automobile).

**4. DEFENDANT'S STATEMENT:**

Yeah, it was me. All me. I did it. No one else. Anyone who saw the guy smashing the s*** out of that car said it looked like me. And who looks like me? Me, that's who. No one else.

**5. VICTIM'S STATEMENT:**

I think he's a mental. The guy who smashed up my car seems like a totally different person from the one who gave himself in. He professed his love for me and when I told him I wasn't interested he went completely batshit. But this guy . . . this guy seems more my type.

## METROPOLITAN POLICE

## POLICE INTERVIEW TRANSCRIPT

**DCI C:** This is DCI Steve Chalmers starting the interview with suspect Rudy Wade at 13.13.

**RW:** I did it. This is suspect Rudy Wade ending the interview at 13.13. Case closed.
[Silence]

**DCI C:** It doesn't work like that.

**RW:** Why? What else do you need?
[Silence]

**DCI C:** Why did you do it?

**RW:** I don't know. Because I needed to do it. If I didn't I would have killed someone . . .
[Silence]

**RW:** . . . again.
[Silence]

**RW:** Mate, I was joking.
[Silence]

**RW:** What are you doing? What are you writing? Ah, mate. Mate. Stop writing. Seriously. Please. Ah balls.

# CURTIS DONOVAN... MIND OF AN ATHLETE

People are always asking me what goes through my mind when i race. it's simple really.

**4TH CORNER**

Oh, there she is again. Yeah. Yup. That's her. Oh Stacey. Time has not been your friend has it? Nah, time has beaten you into a bucket.

**3RD CORNER**

My name's Bane. i'm a badass motherfucka! i crack skulls. Breaking heads and hymens. Don't get in my way, shitheaaaaaaaaaaad. Bane. Bane? Bane Donovan. Nah, too many n's.

**START**

Win. Win. Win. Win. Win. Win. Win. Win. Win. Win. Win.

**LONG STRAIGHT**

Stacey! Her name was Stacey.

**FINISH**

Either 'Yesssss!' or 'Fuuuuuck!'

**2ND CORNER**

Why do I do this? is it fun? What is fun? No. I want to be doing this. Or do I just think i do? Have i made myself believe it? Forced myself to because if i don't like it then...then i've wasted my life. What am i doing? What am i doing with my life?

**1ST CORNER**

Aw shit. Was that...? Fuck. What was her name again? Aw man, come on. She gave you your first hand job. What was it? Jane? Bane? Bane. i ain't never got a wank off no one called Bane. Fuck's sake.

# PENNY DREADFUL

No. 156

4D

Dear Tender Reader, a word of caution prior to our journey into Gammon. We do not put these lines forth as a specimen of the Poetry of the Age, but where my tale is a little wanting in Poetic Fire, it is amply made up for with Dread, Horror and Unspeakable Villainies. Indeed it concerns itself with the thin thread betwixt my Sanity and Curs'd Insanity, and the Spur to my Ruination, the taking of a Scurrilous Scullery Maid and a Puckish Chimney-Sweep intomy employ.

Such was the state of my affairs in the Year of Our Lord 1845, that I had occasion, due to the misfortunate death of my Blessed Aunt Hettie and the very fortunate inheritance of her wealth, to assemble a house. I purchased a stone townhouse in Temple and set about hiring the necessary staff. As unaccustomed as I was to such, as the son of a barber and a midwife, and not wanting to cause ill odour or ignominy with my brethren neighbours, I placed a curt advertisement in one of the cornerpanes of glass in my window. And all was well; momentarily.

Oh, Cursed Knock. Oh, Vile Knock. So thrilling in potential; so odious in Hindsight. When I opened those doors, I opened the very door to Perdition.

In walked a pair in such queer habiliments and alien phraseology that the effect of their sudden appearance was altogether discombobulating. Indeed something in their aspect did foment an air of far-flung lands and future ages in my mind's eye. But had I been thinking rationally, and please believe me reader when I say I was far beyond rationality, I would have recognised in them what they truly were and that was escapees, no doubt, of Bedlam.

The, and I loathe to use this word for fear she hears in some distant dimension and comes for retribution, wench had the Christian appellation of Kelly. Indeed, there was a touch of the Bawdy House about her, but the eyes burnt incandescent with Truth and Honour. However, when she opened those pert lips there did cascade such atrocities that were unknown to my ears, I could not tell whether she was here to serve or to sever.

My visage must have betrayed my bewilderment for her accomplice at this point jumped in as relief interlocutor. Truly he was the Charybdis to her Scylla.

An odd man of such curious countenance, with Leviathan eyebrows and a fright of hair which he wore as the insignia of insouciance. He was an Irishman and a Licentious Libertine, prurient to the point of perversion. He had the singular quiddity of a man constantly finagling something, but of what . . . even now, I struggle to fit words to the sensations – both enlivening and alarming – the pair awakened deep within me. The name this Young Buck gave was Nathan. And now, as I write those letters for the first time since our shared contretemps, the very name makes my Soul strangely ill at ease. I did not so much agree to take them in as bow to their Wills, which were the Stuff of Adamantine. However, I was shortly relieved to learn that this strange duo were not planning to tarry long.

Spoke Nathan: 'Just waiting for a friend, you know? Uh, how do I explain this to you without blowing that Tiny Tim mind of yours? It's like we were on our way somewhere, when to when, not where to where, and we got a flat tyre. Oh fuck! Do you have tyres here? Have you got wheels? Oh shit, Kelly, I think I've just broken history. Look, just don't tell anyone about the whole tyres thing. It'll be our little secret. Just between me and you. Anyway, we're just waiting for a friend to pick us up and bring us back home. Home on the range. Where the beer and the ketamine play. Oh bollocks. Have they invented America yet?'

'I fail to understand your meaning,' I admitted. 'What is this word . . . "fuck"?'

And with that both Satyrs doubled over and spewed forth such terrifying cackling that when it did strike upon the ear it did unnerve me further. Such ominous utterances prick like daggers for the Faint of Heart.

I awoke in night's dark embrace, Terror clutching at my heart. The room was filled with such a foul miasma that I did think the Demonic Prince Beelzebub had visited me to offer an Unholy Treaty. Never had such a stench offended my olfactory equipment before. In a moment of twisted reverie spoke to me a Voice from the darker regions of my mind suggesting that this was not a corporeal smell but the manifestation of my putrifying mind. Oh, if only t'were indeed so.

I lit a candle and barely holding my heart inside my chest, which I held scarcely inside my nightgown, I set forth to investigate. Now, I won't be so puerile of thought or whimsical in style to suggest a Diabolical Confusion of the senses, but verily I could see from where the fetid cloud was emanating: the scullery. No doubt it issued forth from its new occupants, Mistress Kelly and Master Nathan. I shuddered, shook and cautiously proceeded, unaware I was tiptoeing towards my very Ruination.

Oh, Reader. Oh, happy, naïve Reader. Treasure the purity of your sight, treasure it well because there are things of this Earth that once seen cannot be unseen. Such consternation, such loathsome, visceral sights I did witness when I opened that fateful scullery door. All was raucous. The Sylph Kelly retched and gagged, holding a gin-soaked rag to her mouth to mask the putrid plumes of smoke that billowed from the hearth. The Daemon Nathan seemed impervious and frolicked around the room with much gusto, singing in his Celtic brogue: 'What? What's wrong? What? What's wrong?' only stopping his Hellish Jig when he spied me at the door.

'Did we wake you? Ah, sorry about that there, Chief.'

Of a sudden, I could take no more. 'Chief? Chief? I am your Master!'

'Do you hear that, Kelly? Either someone's just come down with a case of the Bertie Big Bollocks or he's just about to show us why he really put us down here in the dungeon. They have ball-gags in these times, do they?'

'Mate, can we just get the fuck out of here? It's rank,' quoth the girl.

'Silence! And tell, Foul Spectres, what source does this Foul Odour come from?! What Devilment? What Trickery is this?'

A Baleful Silence.

The girl at last did tut and roll her eyes and imparted these sinister words: 'It's his effin' jizz sock.'

'Jizz sock?' I repeated, my workaday tongue stumbling over the exotic Incantation.

The girl tutted and her eyes, once again, rolled back in her skull. 'I was asleep and he was . . . he was doing whatever. Then when he finished he threw his jizz sock in the fire. It's well disgusting.'

'Breath it in, folks. It's life in its purest form. Makes me feel . . . alive.' And with that the Fiend resumed his disturbed jig, a Demented Wraith haunting my own dear hearth.

The room began to spin. I felt the Walls of Sanity begin to crumble about me; the Foundations of my Sensibility start to quake. From outside myself I heard my Mind cry: 'Do not! Do not ask what you are about to ask. It is not your quarry nor your concern. Just turn on your heel and walk away. Turn back to the quiet of your bedchamber and forget all you have seen tonight.'

But due to some damned spirit of perversity, I could not heed its warnings. I had to ask . . .

'Pray tell, what is this "jizz sock"?'

Next week! Our terrifying conclusion . . .

# WLTM?

From: Nathan Young <doctorloveandhispenisthermometer@blueyonder.co.uk>
To: Kelly Bailey <m8itskellybaileyyeah@hotmail.co.uk>

I know it hasn't been long since Bruno. And some people may say I'm being insensitive. I get that a lot. Fuckers. But I think you need to get back up on the horse. Not actually a horse. Unless you fancy a horse; then it's grand. Although I think the woman in *Animal Farm* (not that *Animal Farm*) died after doing that.

Anyway, I've been asking around and here are some shortlisted beefcakes:

**Koala:** The perfect rebound. He'd be mad into cuddles. I'd say they'd be very affectionate lovers. I mean, he wouldn't really be great for rutting, if that's what you're into. It'd be more some tantric-type shit. Oh, and I wouldn't let him finger you (claws).

**Penguin:** Again, good rebound material. Funny guy, I'd say. And you can take him to posh restaurants. I'd say he should take you, but I don't think penguins get what restaurants are, conceptually. Also, wouldn't complain if you smelt a bit like...uh...sweat?

**Dolphin:** Maybe you should dip the toe in the waters of Lesbonia? Well, if you got a bit of the taste for the teat a dolphin would be perfect. Apart from the fact that they don't have a set of mamms. Or do they? They're mammals so I guess they do. But then they'd be swimming around the place with two streams of milk streaming behind them. Like an underwater aeroplane. Anyway, whatever. Go for a dolphin because all dolphins are lesbians. Fact. Even the male ones.

**Bear + Shark:** I think you should get a bear and get a shark. Tell them both to meet you down at Wimpy's and when they em fight to see who takes you to the flicks. Go on. Do it. I've a bet to settle.

**Liger:** You need to get with a liger. No one would fuck with you if you're with a liger. You would be an instant 'power couple' around the estate. You could get matching Burberry hats. Also, I've it on good authority that they are generous in the sack... although you might have to train him in one area. Give him a taste for the white meats.

Anyway, hope you don't take this the wrong way. But, to be honest, I've read it back and I don't know how anyone could. This is one of the least selfish emails I've ever sent.

Apart from the bear/shark thing. That's just for me.

Let me know.
Nathan

P.S. Surely someone's made dolphin cheese already, right?

# RICHARD SAUNDERS:
## THE MAN THE MYTH THE LEGEND

My mate Richard Saunders used to film himself taking shits out of trees and then play that 'Ride of the Valkyries' song over it. Apoocalypse Now he'd call it. Richard Saunders, 'The Colonel', is a fucking legend.

Richard Saunders once took so many drugs he convinced himself he was 'only a B-plot character of some television show'. Where does he get this shit from?

Richard Saunders is the only man I have ever met that has slept with someone from every continent. Who the fuck sleeps with someone from Antarctica? Mad bastard.

Richard Saunders has a collection of over fifty dog turds in his shed. And to this day he has never revealed why.

Richard Saunders once got puked on by Shane MacGowan. He laughed and puked back on him. He now has his number in his phone.

Richard Saunders' dad is my dentist.

Richard Saunders once died for four seconds but Death couldn't handle the party.

Richard Saunders only goes to house parties if there's an even number on the door. Or if there's cocaine.

Richard Saunders invented text messages when he was stoned but told no one about it and then when they became popular he thought the phone companies had bugged his mind and th . . . actually that was a really dark perio and we don't like to talk about that.

# SO YOU'VE SUDDENLY BECOME 'A HOMELESS'?

Your mum throws you out because your winning personality 'isn't compatible' with her new boyfriend who's 'loving and tender and kind'...whatever the fuck that means.

**BAGS ON BACK:** You need more than one. Obviously to hold your shit in but also because it makes you walk funny. Like you've killed someone. No one will mess with you in the hostel.

**PHONE:** The most important thing to 'a homeless'. For ringing friends. Or people that you have met a few times. Or once. People that you have met once. Anyone. For ringing anyone for a place to stay. Also, you'd be surprised how much Snake you play as 'a homeless'.

**BIN BAGS:** I actually don't carry anything in here. It just makes you look like a loon. See also: BAGS ON BACK.

**BUSHES:** For food. They're nature's vending machines. But also nature's toilets. So watch out.

**THE RIGHT JEANS:** You don't want to go for anything too distressed, but a bit ripped is a must. I asked No-Teeth Benjamin down at the drop-in and he said it's really in this season.

**SHELTER:** Under an overpass like here is actually surprisingly better than the drop-in. I mean, sure, here you might end up getting bummed in your sleep. But in the drop-in, No-Teeth Benjamin told me he would definitely bum me in my sleep. No contest, really.

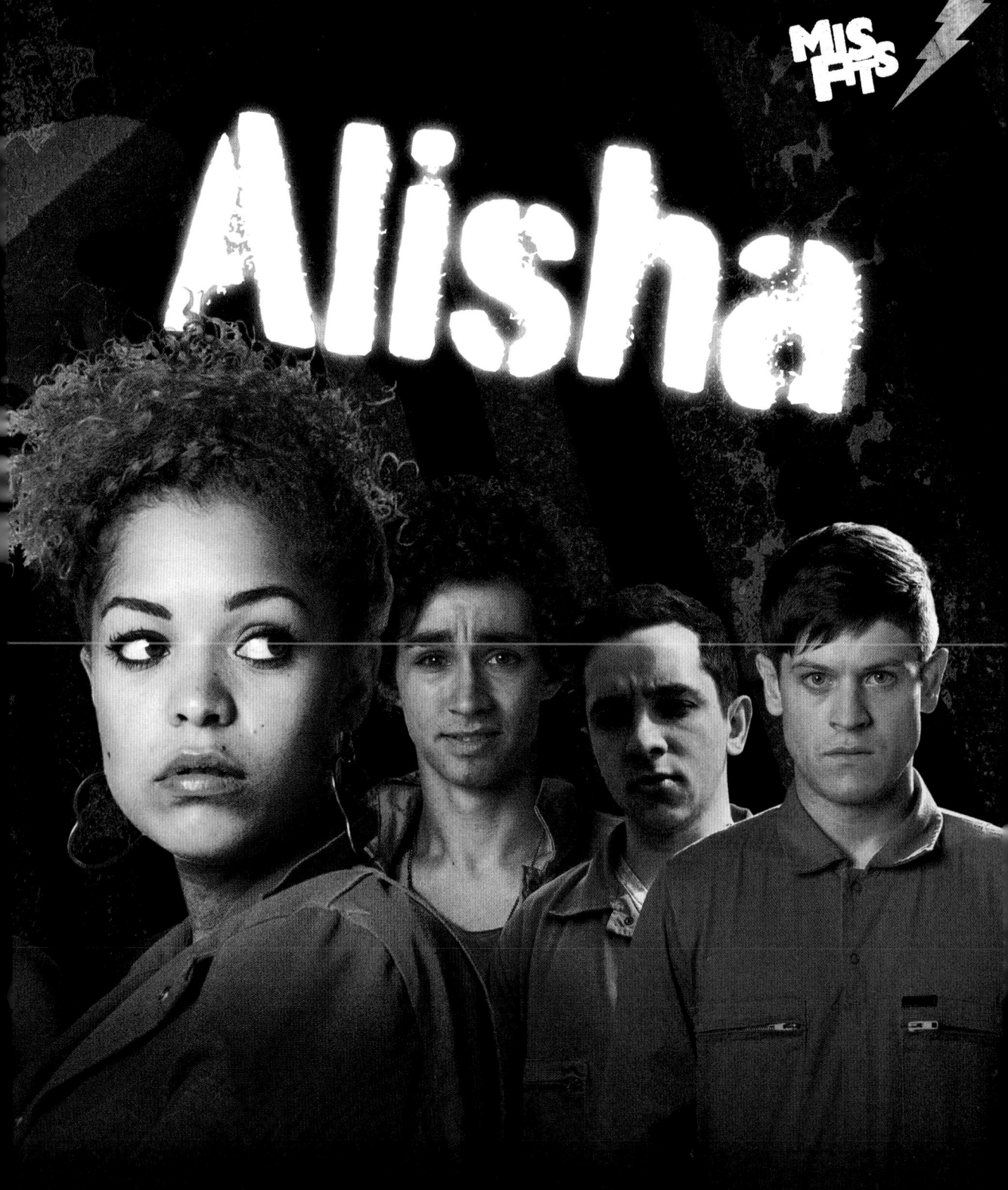

# PERFECTING YOUR LAIR

Having a lair is one thing. But having a lair which is stylish without being too contrived, businesslike without being too sterile, functional as well as fashionable? Only a few can pull that off. Actually, you know what? Don't even bother. If you need to read this, a lair is not for you. Step away from the lair.

**1 DESK**

The only reason I have this in here is so there's something between me and the johns. It's not like I'm writing cheques or my memoirs.

**2 GLASS OF WATER**

I need to put something on the desk.

**3 BOXES**

I keep a lot of my stock in here. It's probably the most functional aspect to my lair (apart from the henchman). So it's even more annoying when Dot, the woman who comes to tidy up for me, puts all her cleaning shit in there. I keep on telling her, 'Dot, I'm running a business here.' But she's old. A friend of the family. What am I supposed to do?

**4 SUIT**

Okay, not part of the furniture but it's more important than the chair I'm sitting

in. You know what they say, the suit makes the man. And the man makes the lair. So really . . .

**5 LIGHTING**

This is key. You want moody, mysterious but with an element of danger. Some-where between stage production of *Sexy Beast* and darkroom in a gay nightclub.

**6 SOLITARY CHAIR**

It fucks with their minds. 'What's it for? Am I supposed to sit in it? Why's it in the corner? What's it facing? Fuuuuuuck.'

**7 FLOOR NUMBER**

Crucial. You want either the basement or the penthouse. Who ever had a lair on the first floor of somewhere? Newsagents. That's who.

1

# PENIS, SCISSORS, TWAT

Are you and a chum at loggerheads? Is a mate vexing you with intolerable requests? What you need is an arcane decider game. Dispense with any ill will by placing your fate in the mystic algorithms of *Penis, Scissors, Twat*.

1. There are three symbols to be played with your hand – the precise penis, the crafty scissors and the stalwart twat – each is lord over one and craven at the sight of another.

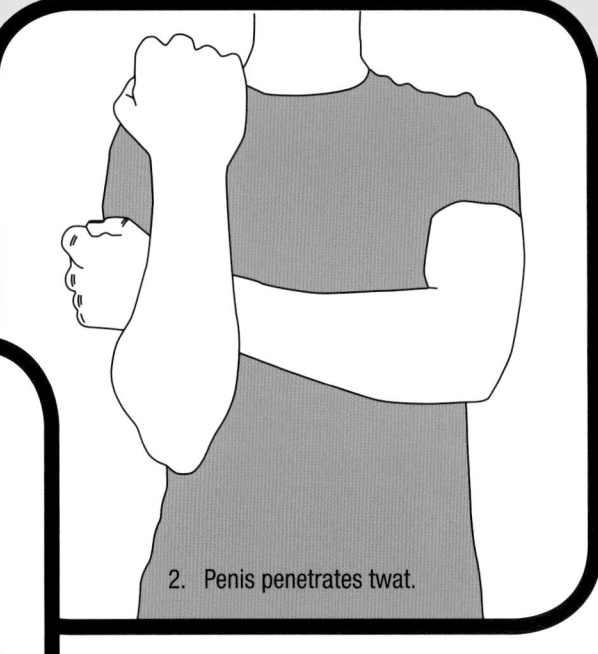

2. Penis penetrates twat.

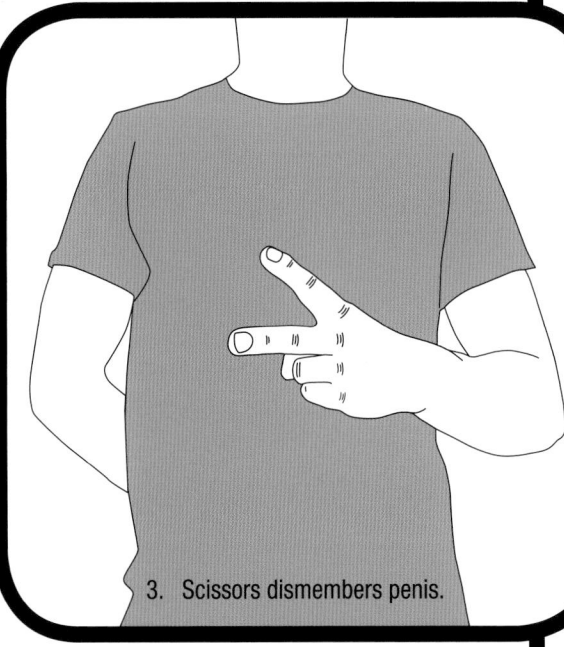

3. Scissors dismembers penis.

4. Twat consumes scissors.

5. You and your sparring partner raise a fist each and swing down on the count until three . . . at which point you reveal your play.
6. *Penis, Scissors, Twat*'s decision is final and absolute.

# THERE IS NO HIGHER AUTHORITY.

# chat

Inbox | Settings

## Rudy Wade

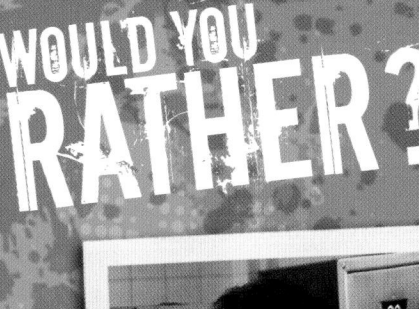

### Search

- Alisha
- Sally
- Hot4u
- Kelly
- Nathan
  Captain Spun kw
- Curtis
- Cyndie
- Dave-O
- Elyssa
- Jimmy Jay
- Simon

# WOULD YOU RATHER?

## Curtis

✉ Email     ☎ Call

*<Rudy Wade has joined the conversation>*

| | |
|---|---|
| Curtis Donovan: | Alright? |
| Rudy Wade: | Maaaaaaaaaaaaaaaaaaaaaaaaaaaaaaaaaa |
| Curtis Donovan: | What? |
| Rudy Wade: | aaaaaaaaaaaaaaaaaaaaaaaaate |
| Curtis Donovan: | What do you want Rudy?! |
| Rudy Wade: | You know the way? |
| Curtis Donovan: | The way what? |
| Rudy Wade: | The way you can go from him to quim? Hello? |
| | Curtis mate, I think your 'puter is fucked. |
| Curtis Donovan: | No. I'm here, Rudy. |
| Rudy Wade: | Good stuff. So about your mangina . . . |
| Curtis Donovan: | What about it, Rudy? |
| Rudy Wade: | Have you ever played Would You Rather? |
| Curtis Donovan: | No. |
| Rudy Wade: | Aw! You haven't? You're missing out, mate. It's simple as fook. I give you two things and you pick which one you'd rather. |
| Curtis Donovan: | Yeah. I fucking get it. |
| Rudy Wade: | Alright, easy there, Mister Menstrual. |
| Curtis Donovan: | Just ask. |
| Rudy Wade: | Okay, round one, chachi. Would you rather . . . pink or blue? You there? |
| Curtis Donovan: | Blue. |
| Rudy Wade: | Thought so. Okay. Easy start. Would you rather have . . . camel toe or moose knuckle? |
| Curtis Donovan: | WTF is moose knuckle??? |
| Rudy Wade: | The boy version of camel toe. When people can lip-read your donger through tight trou. |
| Curtis Donovan: | Jesus. |
| Rudy Wade: | Not an option. |
| Curtis Donovan: | I don't know. Moose knuckle? |
| Rudy Wade: | Figures, big boy. |
| Curtis Donovan: | Fuck off. Do you actually need anything? |
| Rudy Wade: | Yes. An answer. To would you rather . . . really big breasts or really big balls? |
| Curtis Donovan: | Why would I want really big balls? |
| Rudy Wade: | Why would you not want big balls? |
| Curtis Donovan: | I'm off. |
| Rudy Wade: | Okay, no, wait. I've a serious question. |
| Curtis Donovan: | What? |
| Rudy Wade: | A permanent lob-on or a permanent wide-on? |

*<Curtis Donovan left the conversation>*

# REGARDEZ!

## Monsieur Grand Fromage

C'est incroyable.
Le Big Daddy de produits laitiers.
Il met le lait dans le café …
avec sa tête.

5 December 2011

# WERTHAM Weekly

**Making Local News M...**

(who ...

## Wertham Weekly Weekender:
### RATE A DATE

Every week we ask two loved-up lovebirds in a local restaurant how their date is going. This week we visited 'It's a Pisa Up' and quizzed new couple Seth (26, local entrepreneur) and Kelly (22, rocket scientist [obviously joking])

### SETH ON KELLY

*Before the date, what were you hoping for?*
Nothing. I learned not to expect anything with Kelly. She'll just prove you wrong.
*What are you chatting about?*
My gin and tonic, the business I run, stuff.
*Any awkward moments so far?*
My gin and tonic.
*Good table manners?*
Of course. Why did you ask that? Is that supposed to be a joke?
*Best thing about her?*
I think if you don't leave in the next two minutes you'll find out.
*Would you introduce her to your friends?*
I don't have many friends. And I like to keep my business associates separate.
*Could she meet the parents?*
She could. But why would she?
*And . . . have you kissed?*

You're pushing it.
*If you could change one thing about the evening so far, what would it be?*
I'd have maybe ordered a whisky.
*Marks out of 10?*
We're done here.

### KELLY ON SETH

*Before the date, what were you hoping for?*
I was hoping he'd finger me and buy me a packet of crisps.
*What type of question is that, mate?*
*What are you chatting about?*
This fucking weird-looking paedo. And then he came up to us and started asking us questions.
*Any awkward moments so far?*
Naw, mate. Unless you're going to ask if you can come home with us too.

*Good table manners?*
Him? Yeah. Dead posh. Look

at his little gin and tonic and all.
*Best thing about him?*
Uh, look at him. He's a big ride.
*Would you introduce him to your friends?*
Actually, I might hold off for the moment, yeah? He's met them before.
*Could he meet the parents?*
He could. But he could be made minced meat by my dad.
*And . . . have you kissed?*
Get to fuck, you sicko. What? Are you wanking under that raincoat?
*If you could change one thing about the evening so far, what would it be?*
Everything's perfect apart from the wanking raincoat paedo.
*Marks out of 10?*
Mate . . . that's fucking creepy. Seriously, yeah? Get out.

# MISFITS

# WHAT'S YOUR SECRET POWER?

## 1 Someone cuts in line at the cinema. Do you:

A) Tell everyone to relax, then explain in a calm voice to the person why it is unfair for them to do that.

B) Blow some pollen their way and hope that they have hay fever.

C) Tap them on the shoulder then, when they look, go the other way and do the same until they get confused and leave.

D) Shoot lasers at them from your eyes.

## 2 A work colleague is upset because someone ate the cake that she was keeping in the fridge. Do you:

A) Talk her down and suggest the two of you go out of the office for cake. Your treat.

B) Back her up and threaten your co-workers with cacti.

C) Suggest to whoever it was that they go for a run with you to work off the extra weight, thereby shaming them into confessing.

D) Shoot lasers at her from your eyes because you know it was you.

## 3 A friend has just got dumped. Do you:

A) Talk to her in a calm and sincere way and explain that her boyfriend was a dickhead. Maybe suggest smoking some weed.

B) Grow a weed plant. Then smoke it with her.

C) Bring her a bag of speed.

D) Go over to her ex's house and shoot him with lasers from your eyes.

# What do our personalities tell us about the type of superhero we would be?

## Take our two-minute quiz to find out . . .

**MIS FITS**

ANSWERS: *if you answered mostly...* **'A';** You would have the power to psychically chill people out. You've a very calming effect on people and they really appreciate it. You must be a good friend to have around in a crisis. **'B';** You would have the ability to control plants. You're always on the lookout for Mother Nature and encourage potential friends to reduce their carbon footprint **'C';** You would have supersonic speed. You are always on the go, whizzing around. Your social life must be non-stop. Don't forget to take time to smell the roses. **'D';** You would have the power to shoot lasers out of your eyes.

**4**

**You get stuck in an elevator on your way to an important meeting. Do you:**

A) Call the meeting and tell them calmly that you'll be late. Then suggest to everyone in the lift that you sing some songs.

B) Freak out because you are in a lift with no plants.

C) Start running around in circles in the lift, hoping that you will generate a whirlwind and raise the lift up to your desired floor.

D) Shoot your way out with lasers from your eyes.

**5**

**You are in a National Trust park and you see someone littering. Do you:**

A) Tell yourself to 'take a chill pill' and pick up the litter.

B) Start crying and push a tree down on top of him.

C) Decide there is nothing you can really add to this situation.

D) Shoot everything around you with lasers from your eyes.

177

# The Diary
## of Rudy Too

*Rudy stay away. For your own good!*

*Too much truth in here.*

## Monday 14th December

Had to stand in for Rudy today and do his community service. Just so he could go off and have intercourse with some poor girl with low self-esteem. Honestly, I don't know where he finds them. Or how he can look them in the eye while 'making love' when he knows he's just going to leave them straight away after. Pah! Making love? As if he knows the meaning of the word.

I know I don't. All I know is loneliness.

Picking up rubbish on the side of the road did make me think though. It's a good analogy for life. The road is time. You are you. The rubbish is figurative rubbish. The teenagers mocking you while you do it are your emotions. And the man who spent the day staring at you and jangling his keys in his pocket is Death. Always watching over, coming at any minute.

Tell me you didn't say anything to Jacob! That fucker won't leave me alone now for a month.

Lucky → (I usually don't... if you know what I mean? Eh eh?)

Rudy never came home last night. I imagine he's dead. There's no way he'd stay with a girl until she wakes up in the morning. He's not that decent. Not that warm. Not that loving. Not that much of a quim. I am. a bell-end

I want to be. I would be warm . . . if life hadn't made me so cold. I would be loving . . . if I had someone to love. I would be decent . . . if I knew people that needed me to be decent. But I don't. All is empty. All is lost.

All has apparently crawled up your arse and made you a miserable gonad.

I also saw a cat that someone had dressed as a snowman. Tragically fucking hilarious!

If you meant 'dead' as in 'his balls must be totally empty', then yes.

## Wednesday 16th December

Today I plunged to new depths of abject misery. I woke up (unfortunately) and went for my breakfast. I opened the fridge and found nothing but a single bottle of urine. Which sums up my life entirely. Well, if the bottle had a suspect lump on it then it would have summed it up perfectly.

Next thing I knew, I received a clatter around my head. That animal I share a face with roared at me, 'Don't even think about drinking that. I need it.' I assured him I was not going to drink his urine and pressed him on what it was for.' That ********* probation worker is doing drug tests next week and I'm planning on getting mad out of it tonight . . . need that liquid gold to pass. Thought I should take it this morning while I'm clean as a whistle.' After I reminded him of his speed binge the night previous he walked out, suggesting I get rid of it or drink it, it's no good to me. I am doing neither. It's his problem.

UPDATE: I couldn't sleep so I threw it out. Textbook.

Nothing really happened today. Today I woke up and I was miserable. I had a massive crank (cry and wank). Basically my problem is I live with a much fitter and more hung version of myself. It's tough always seeing this handsome, donkey-donged Rudy walking around. Especially when my face is even more shrivelled than my pecker. Which is very shrivelled.

I should probably learn from the other Rudy to loosen up. Take a chill pill . . . or better yet, some meow-meow. Actually, no. I better stay away from meow-meow. My mate Richard Saunders, a mate of the other Rudy, had a three-day comedown from meow-meow once that only ended when he went to hospital because he was crying solid salt since he'd being crying for so long. Anyway, I digress. I need to cheer the fuck up.

Has anyone seen my Gary?
Your Mum loves you, Gary.
Whatever's happened you
know you can always come
home, Gargar.

Have you seen this man?
Missing in mysterious
circumstances. Have
possible leads but need
evidence. Please contact
Sally on 555-67-68.

**Have you seen this woman?**
Missing in mysterious circumstances.
Please contact the Wertham
community service office with
any information.

**This one too. Anyone seen him?**
Linked to wider web of missing
persons. Could possibly be involved
in some financial scam gone wrong.
Any information on Shaun (or what
the financial scam could be) please
contact the Wertham community
service office.

**Laura?
Seriously? You too?**

HAS ANYONE SEEN MY EX-GIRLFRIEND?

Missing since two weeks ago. Tanya if you're out there I was wrong to do that. I was a dick. I just want you back. I want to make you my queen. You have so much to live for.

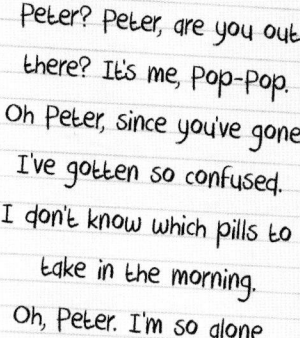

Peter? Peter, are you out there? It's me, Pop-Pop. Oh Peter, since you've gone I've gotten so confused. I don't know which pills to take in the morning. Oh, Peter. I'm so alone.

**Missing. Entire Wertham Community Cheerleading Squad.**

Please contact. Sectionals approaching. Come on girls!

Missing. A good man. His congregation is worried no good has come to their shepherd. No doubt some corrupt degenerates have led him down a path to ruination. Call me.

WANTED.

INFORMATION ON MY GRAN'S CAT. POSSIBLE WITNESS TO A MURDER. MR MIGGLES, IF YOU'RE OUT THERE, I DON'T BELIEVE A WORD THE CORONER SAYS. THERE'S NO WAY YOU WOULD HAVE EATEN SOME OF GRAN'S FACE. I KNOW SOMEONE PUT YOU UP TO IT.

Listen up, carolling cock-knockers. This is myself, Marnie and Nathan Junior's first Christmas together as a family. So we thought it'd be a nice family thing to do to invite ye c*nts to our place for Christmas dinner. So on the big day come down to celebrate with us, you big pack of jingle bell-ends.

Nathan.

P.S. Bring booze. And also Christmas dinner.

6 a.m. — As is the tradition with small children, we'll be getting up at the crack of dawn to open Nathan Jr's presents. Since he's nowt but a shitting bean bag at the moment I'll be assuming opening duties. Presents to be provided by his aunts and uncles.

7 a.m. — Traditional Christmas morning tequila shots.

8 a.m. — This time I have put aside for ye to gaze upon Nathan Jr. I will be in the next room. Alone with Marnie. Several times.

9 a.m. — Still emptying my sleigh-balls.

10 a.m. — Christmas Day Breakfast: Salmon. Failing that: chocolate truffles. Failing that: more tequila.

11 a.m. — First drinks of the day: Fuck's Fizz (Buckfast tonic wine + orange juice). Then gifts. This year myself and Marnie are providing the gift of hospitality. And life (Nathan Jr).

12 p.m. — First fight. No doubt one of ye fuckers will bring a gift that's not cash equivalent to 'life'. Typical.

1 p.m. — Skype our other (lesser) families. Not like our close family here. Bring your laptop, Barry.

2 p.m. — Traditional Christmas pre-dinner drinks and drugs (tepid wine and ketamine).

3 p.m. — Christmas dinner. Kelly, if you're the one providing the food then maybe Curtis should carve the chicken nuggets?

4 p.m. — After-dinner games: 'Pin the Dick on the Donkey', 'Non-Consensual Sex in the Dark'. All the family favourites.

5 p.m. — Second fight. I'm betting old pantysniffer will cheat at 'Non-Consensual Sex in the Dark'. Shifty eyes.

6 p.m. — THE HOUR OF LOADED SILENCE.

7 p.m. — Third fight. The reckoning. A year's worth of shit bubbles out. Some real passive-aggressive sinister shit going on here. Marnie, you should probably leave the room with Nathan Jr.

8 p.m. — Pudding.

9 p.m. — Reconciliation.

10 p.m. — Movie time.

10.07 p.m. — Fourth fight. TBC.

10.09 p.m. — Carols.

11 p.m. — Love-in. Back-rubs. Maintaining eye contact just that bit too long. Hugs. The good stuff.

# The Lost Scripts
## written by Howard Overman

There are many casualties along the road from script one to screen. Sometimes it's a character that isn't quite right or a storyline that doesn't totally gel, or a gag that may or may not be deemed 'inappropriate' and bordering on 'illegal'. Suffice to say we've had to lose our fair share... plenty of plots, stacks of story, annals of anal. Here Howard Overman, the show's creator, takes us on a tour of some never-before-seen, uh, scenes that didn't make the cut.

## LUCKY GUY

After Alisha had come to terms with her original power in Series 1, I always had the intention of telling a story in Series 2 about how she meets someone who isn't affected by her power, someone who has a super-power which negates Alisha's power. I wanted this to be a guy that Alisha fancied, so it would impact on her relationship with Curtis, her boyfriend at the time.

The idea I came up with was Lucky Guy – someone who was struck in the storm and became the luckiest guy in the world – so lucky that everything went his way, including the ability to touch Alisha without her power kicking in.

The story kicked off with Alisha meeting Lucky Guy again and falling in love with him. She had missed physical contact and affection since she was struck in the storm, which was the basis of problems in her relationship with Curtis. But to give the story an additional twist, unbeknownst to Lucky Guy, there was also Unlucky Guy. This was a sort of yin-yang idea – every time Lucky Guy got lucky, Unlucky Guy had a parallel helping of bad luck.

So I wrote the script...but apart from a great climax where Lucky Guy and Alisha jump off of the community centre roof and luckily land on a mattress, it just didn't work. Luck turned out to be a tough concept to base a power on, and splitting the power between Lucky Guy and Unlucky Guy was over-complicated.

But as I was realising that the story wasn't going to work, I had an idea. I knew that Superhoodie was going to be Simon from the future, but what if he, rather than Lucky Guy, was the one who was able to touch Alisha? What if he was the one who Alisha fell in love with? It was one of those ideas that I knew straight away was going to work. And so the Superhoodie time-loop love-story was born, thanks to another story that didn't work out.

I still like the idea of a luck-based power...I haven't managed to make it work so far, but you never know...

INT. BAR – NIGHT

A cool, retro games bar – table football, pool tables etc.

ALISHA's waiting for her drinks at the bar. There's a bit of a commotion nearby. ALISHA sees a beautiful GIRL tying a blindfold over JACK's eyes (early-twenties, handsome, expensively but stylishly dressed). The BARMAN and various YOUNG PEOPLE watch with interest.

The GIRL turns JACK so his back is to the dartboard across the other side of the pub. JACK raises a dart to his lips, kisses it, then casually throws the dart over his shoulder...

The dart sails through the air...and hits the bull's-eye on the dartboard, dead-centre. SPECTATORS react with amazement. ALISHA takes this in.

JACK raises his blindfold, doesn't even check to see whether he hit his mark. The BARMAN is stunned...

                    BARMAN
          What?...How did you do that?

                    JACK
I picture myself doing it, then I do it. It's like some Zen mind shit.

(The BARMAN's dubious...)

                    BARMAN
          It's a fluke.

(The BARMAN reluctantly hands over a bottle of champagne to JACK, then heads off to serve another CUSTOMER. JACK sees ALISHA eyeing him curiously...)

                    JACK
          So what did you think?

(ALISHA responds with a withering look...)

                    ALISHA
          That's really impressive.

(ALISHA goes to pick up her drinks to head off...)

                    JACK
          Don't go. Have some champagne...

(JACK reaches out to grab ALISHA's hand. She instinctively pulls away...)

                    ALISHA
          Don't...!

                    2.
(But it's too late; JACK's grabbed ALISHA's hand. But to her amazement, nothing happens – her power doesn't kick in. ALISHA looks at JACK, who's simply smiling at her...)

                    ALISHA (CONT'D)
                    (stunned)
            You're touching me...?

(JACK withdraws his hand...)

                    JACK
            Sorry. I was just being friendly...

(Seeking confirmation of what just happened, ALISHA reaches out and
touches the side of JACK's neck. Again, her power doesn't kick in.
JACK's bemused by her strange behaviour...)

                    ALISHA
            How are you doing that?

                    JACK
            I don't know...What is it I'm doing?

(ALISHA suddenly feels self-conscious, withdraws her hand...)

                    ALISHA
            Nothing.

(ALISHA picks up her drinks to leave...)

                    JACK
            Have a drink with me.

                    ALISHA
            I'm with my boyfriend.

(JACK takes this in...)

                    JACK
            He's a lucky guy.

(ALISHA isn't sure how to respond. She heads off. JACK stares after
her...)

(On the dart Jack threw, sticking out of the bull's-eye on the dartboard.
The dart comes loose, falls through the air in slow motion, tip first...
straight into the beautiful GIRL's big toe. Slow motion close up on a
horribly graphic impact. A tiny blood splatter...We come out of slow
motion as the GIRL screams...CURTIS is looking over toward the commotion
that is now surrounding the GIRL. ALISHA arrives with the drinks...)

                    3.
                    CURTIS
            What's that about?

                    ALISHA
            I don't know.

(ALISHA looks round, catches JACK's eye. He's standing there, alone –
doesn't appear to be with anyone. ALISHA's intrigued and troubled by the
encounter.)

# DRUG REVERSAL

I'd always liked the idea that the gang's powers could be reversed by taking drugs. I came up with a story where the gang took acid and ended up in a weird parallel universe where they were mirror images of their regular selves – a Misfits take on a classic superhero trope.

Here's how the story panned out. Nathan got some super-strong acid off his dealer and spiked all of the gang, including guest character Lily who had the power to heal. Soon they all found themselves in a world in which everything we had come to know about the gang was reversed.

Everyone who touched Alisha called her a skanky slut instead of wanting to have sex with her, Kelly was compelled to uncontrollably babble her own thoughts instead of hearing what other people were thinking, Curtis could fast-forward time instead of re-winding it, Nathan had brittle bone disease instead of being immortal, and Simon was Mr. Confident instead of being invisible. As a result of their different powers the gang's personalities were completely different: Alisha lost her sexual confidence, Nathan was a quivering wreck and Simon was the leader of the gang with everyone competing for his attention. For some reason I decided that this Simon should have a moustache, and that Nathan had copied him and grown one too. It seemed funny at the time.

```
(INT. CHEWY'S FLAT (LOUNGE) - DAY
A cool, chaotic flat. Background music plays on the stereo. Open on
SASHA (early-twenties, nicely tanned, beautiful) lying on the sofa.
She's wearing a long T-shirt, which just about covers her knickers.
NATHAN takes a sneaky peek at SASHA, eying her bare legs. CURTIS
looks on as CHEWY (mid-twenties, cool, stoner) weighs out a few bags
of grass...)

                    CHEWY
     Can I interest you fellas in some super-strong, trip-
     your-nuts-off liquid acid?

                    NATHAN
     Liquid acid? That sounds made up...
```

CHEWY

This is the stuff they dip the tabs in. One hundred
percent pure, undiluted. It will fry your mind
and fuck you sideways.

NATHAN

I'm up for some of that.

CURTIS

I think I'll pass.

(CHEWY rummages around, trying to find the liquid acid...)

CHEWY

You won't regret it...(realising that's not entirely true)
You might. Depends how it goes...

While CHEWY's distracted, NATHAN leans over and peeks up
SASHA's T-shirt - gets a peek at her cute knickers. CURTIS catches
his eye, reacts with disdain... NATHAN suddenly falls off the chair,
crashes to the floor, lands in an undignified heap. CHEWY looks round,
sees NATHAN sprawled on the floor...

CHEWY (CONT'D)

What're you doing?

(NATHAN hesitates, knows this could go very badly wrong...)

NATHAN

I'm break dancing...

(NATHAN busts some break dance moves on the floor. He's not very good,
and there's not enough space...)

2.

(CURTIS and CHEWY stare, bemused. NATHAN smashes a mug, leaps to his
feet - finishes with a flourish. He sees CHEWY staring at him, gestures
to the mug...)

NATHAN (CONT'D)

That'll be fine - a little bit of super glue...
(miming sticking the pieces together)

(EXT. STREET — DAY
NATHAN and CURTIS walking alongside a wall. NATHAN's
examining a small bottle of liquid acid...)

                         CURTIS
                       (sarcastic)
               Nice moves.

(The sound of a car engine grows louder, approaching fast...)

                         NATHAN
            That's the thing about me. I'm very good in a crisis.

(Alerted by the engine noise, CURTIS turns to see a distinctive red
car has mounted the pavement and is bearing down on them. CURTIS
shoves NATHAN into the shelter of an alcove in the wall as the car
speeds past, just missing them. NATHAN and CURTIS look round to see
the car continuing down the pavement. It hits DORIS (eighties) as she
pulls her shopping cart. A horrific impact. The car speeds on, smashing
into a rubbish bin as it goes...DORIS lies on the floor, her limbs
twisted at horrible angles. NATHAN and CURTIS look down at her. NATHAN
looks at the red car, speeding into the distance. He's speechless,
vaguely gestures to DORIS, as though the driver of the car may not
have noticed what he just did...)

                    NATHAN (CONT'D)
            I thought I was a bad driver...

                         CURTIS
                       (appalled)
               I think she's dead.

(NATHAN looks at DORIS, feels for her...)

                         NATHAN
            At least it was quick, and painless...

(Blood sprays from DORIS' mouth as she takes her last breath in utter agony. CURTIS and NATHAN recoil, aghast. NATHAN revises his assessment of the circumstances...)

> NATHAN (CONT'D)
>
> It was relatively quick...

(DORIS lets out a long, unbearably slow, agonised gasp...through which NATHAN grimaces...and then DORIS finally dies. NATHAN breathes out, relieved. He sees a packet of KitKats among the groceries that have spilt from the shopping basket onto the pavement and picks them up...)

> NATHAN (CONT'D)
>
> You want a KitKat...?

(NATHAN and CURTIS are suddenly pushed aside...by LILY (early twenties, cute, wearing a nurse's uniform), who appears on the scene like a super-hero. LILY squats over DORIS and starts to give her the kiss of life...)

> NATHAN (CONT'D)
>
> I was just about to do that...

(But then NATHAN and CURTIS react with shock as they realise this is no ordinary kiss of life. LILY is snogging DORIS, with tongues, really going for it - exploring her mouth...)

> NATHAN (CONT'D)
>
> ...not so much that...more...(makes a vague chest pumping motion)

(But then DORIS' eyes snap open as she comes back to life. CURTIS and NATHAN are utterly stunned...)

> LILY
>
> (to DORIS)
>
> It's okay. You're going to be all right...

(LILY looks up, a little blood around her mouth, sees NATHAN and CURTIS staring, stunned. She smiles...)

> LILY (CONT'D)
>
> Hi.